ESSENTIAL
KENNEL DESIGN

By David Key

1

ESSENTIAL KENNEL DESIGN

First published in 2000 by David Key

Grateful acknowledgement is made to the following for allowing copyright permission to reproduce information on:

Croner Publications: Sections 1.4, 1.5, 1.6, 1.7, 1.8, 1.9, 1.10, 1.11, 1.12, 1.13, 1.14, 2.11, 4.4, 5.1, 5.2, 5.3, 5.4, 5.5, 5.6, 5.7, 5.8, 5.9. - from their manuals: Premises Management & Waste Management.

Construction Industry Training Board: for information on Noise, section 3.14.

Building Services and Equipment by F Hall: published by Pearson Education Ltd. for information on ventilation & water services.

The Blue Cross Animal Welfare Charity: for their permission to use the photographs used to illustrate kennel fittings and materials.

Printed and bound by: **Uniskill Ltd,**
Unit A & D Oakwood
Oakfields Industrial Estate
Enysham
Witney
OX8 1TH.
Tel: 01865 883655
Fax: 01865 881244

All photographs by David Key, including jacket photographs in memory of 'Kim'.

ISBN: 0 9538002 0 2

Contents

Acknowledgements

Introduction

SECTION ONE – Purchase & Construction

1.1	Site Location
1.2	Purchase of Existing Kennels
1.3	Green Field Site
1.4	Planning Permissions
1.5	Time Limits
1.6	Planning Fees
1.7	Enforcement of Planning Control
1.8	Building Regulations
1.9	Building Notice
1.10	Building Control Inspection Process
1.11	Construction (Design and Management) Regulation 1994
1.12	Building Progress Chart
1.13	Demolition
1.14	Trees and Tree Preservation Orders

SECTION TWO – Ancillary Buildings & Equipment

2.1	Site Layout
2.2	Aspect
2.3	Reception Building
2.4	Isolation
2.5	Admissions Unit
2.6	Zoning
2.7	Car Park
2.8	Laundry
2.9	Storage Facility
2.10	Refuse Area
2.11	Incinerator (Law)
2.12	Disabled Toilet

SECTION THREE – Kennel Buildings & Finishes

3.1	Architecture
3.2	Thermal Insulation
3.3	CIEH Regulations
3.4	Kennel Sizes and Types
3.5	Large Open Exercise Runs
3.6	Floor Finishes
3.7	Wall Finishes
3.8	Kennel Metalwork and Associated Items
3.9	Kennel Lighting
3.10	Roof Coverings
3.11	Kennel Heating Systems
3.12	Ventilation
3.13	Condensation (dehumidification)
3.14	Acoustic Measures – Internal/External
3.15	Stress and Stress Reduction Measures
3.16	Kennel Drainage Systems
3.17	Kitchen Facilities
3.18	Disinfectants
3.19	Cleaning Systems
3.20	**SUMMARY - MODERN KENNEL DESIGN**

SECTION FOUR – Infrastructure

4.1	Main Utility Supplies
4.2	Fire Protection
4.3	Site Drainage Systems
4.4	Faeces Disposal
4.5	Landscaping – Trees near buildings

SECTION FIVE - Legislation

5.0   Health & Safety
5.1   Health & Safety at Work Act
5.2   Accidents at Work
5.3   Personal Protective Equipment Regulations
5.4   Disability Discrimination Act 1995
5.5   Environmental Protection Act 1990
5.6   The Gas Safety (Installation & Use) Regulations 1994
5.7   Electricity at Work Regulations
5.8   Fire Precautions (Workplace) Regulations 1997
5.9   Control of Substances Hazardous to Health Regulations 1994

SECTION SIX – Suppliers & Useful Addresses

David Key

David Key has been involved with animals for over 30 years.
His interest started whilst still at school by helping out with a friend's show kennels, later this progressed to working at local boarding kennels.

A combination of animal work and practical skills developed into an interest in buildings, particularly relating to animal accommodation.

After working at a zoo he joined The Blue Cross in 1985. He has been the Works Manager for The Blue Cross Animal Welfare Charity since 1986 and is responsible for the charity's buildings and property at their homing and equine centres.

Acknowledgements

The original idea of this book started in early 1998 with the specific aim to produce a few pages of tips and guidance to the large number of people who telephone me to ask for advice and information on products, materials etc. Since its conception the idea evolved and expanded into the book you are about to read.

I am also indebted to Barry Coupe, Alex Darvill and Ian McLean of Forum Architects for their time and patience in preparing the drawings and plans used throughout the book and their professional advice, which was so freely given.
        I would like to thank Julie Sellors (APBC) for her advice on the finer points of kennel management and particularly the article relating to stress in the kennel environment.
        My grateful thanks also go to Diana Stimson for her invaluable contribution of proof-reading.

Most of all, my special thanks go to Kay who provided the support, encouragement and reassurance throughout the development of this book.

INTRODUCTION

The quality of kennels has evolved over the years, but has jumped significantly in the past three or four. A far greater emphasis is now being placed on the animal, rather than merely providing a secure place for it to stay or for the ease and convenience of the staff.

The book will hopefully, give an insight to all people involved with dogs, whether boarding and breeding kennel owners, charities, welfare centres, architects and surveyors, to the changes in design and options available to them. I must stress that it is not a technical manual but a general guide and overview of systems and designs that I have seen used.

The title of the book is fraught with danger; what is good design and specification? Is it, large well-designed kennels, spacious exercise runs, quality enthusiastic staff, a pleasant country location, or a small 'homely' establishment?

In fact, quality kennels can be a mix of many ideas, but I believe that a well-run establishment with quality, caring, enthusiastic staff can overcome many design faults in order to provide a high level of care to the animals and equally to the public. The fact that the buildings have been constructed to a high standard can only be beneficial and help to improve the running of the property.

Today, life has been made far easier with specialist architects and surveyors who have greatly improved the standard of kennel specification and design. They, along with animal welfare organisations have helped to remove the notion that kennels only need to provide a secure environment with little emphasis being placed on the animals' needs and requirements.

Hopefully, by the end of this book you will see how quality design and specification is extremely important and can reduce long-term expenditure, without losing the caring quality that is so important.

David Key

1.1 SITE LOCATION

One of the greatest difficulties is in choosing the correct site for _your_ requirements. These requirements are very subjective, but the important point to remember is they should take into account your needs in ten years' time; not only the next two years.

One of the first decisions you have to make is whether you opt for a 'green field' site or purchase existing kennels. Both options have merits for and against.

In order to highlight the pros and cons for both options, I have listed some of the more salient points:

1.2 PURCHASE OF EXISTING KENNELS

Obviously if you go down this road it guarantees you an existing client base with an audited income with existing kennels and infrastructure. The down side is the payment for the 'goodwill'. This is a negotiable sum and relates to the popularity of an established business, which is treated as a saleable asset. This varies from business to business and can be a substantial amount.

Some of the questions that _you_ need to ask and satisfy yourself that this is the correct establishment to purchase are:

- Is the location the right one for my needs?

- Is the existing licence adequate? Does it have any spare capacity for any proposed future expansion?

- What cost is involved to bring the buildings up to _your_ required standard?

- Is the site suitable for expansion and development? Will the local planning authority allow any further expansion?

- Is there sufficient car parking?

- Are the existing kennels and associated buildings suitable for your requirements?

- Do the kennels comply with current CIEH standards? The Chartered Institute of Environmental Health (CIEH) is the licensing arm of the local council. In order to obtain an animal boarding licence the establishment needs to ensure that they comply with guidelines set by the CIEH.

- Is the infrastructure adequate for the current demands being imposed on it, i.e. electricity, gas, water supply and drainage. Is there any spare capacity for future expansion? All of these areas are the lifeblood of the premises, without them life can be made extremely difficult. I will talk about these in greater detail later.

- Do the kennel floors slope the correct way i.e. into a drain system?

- Have there been any complaints to the local authority or any restrictions imposed by the local authority regarding noise, opening times, vehicular/foot traffic, pollution etc?

- Does the site have the right amount of residential accommodation? Is there suitable space available to construct additional accommodation if required?

- Access - Can the access be maintained all year? Does the land suffer from flooding making part of the property unusable during the winter months?

The list is endless, I believe that some of the most informative information can be obtained about an existing property, not purely from a surveyor's report, but from spending time watching the kennel staff go about their daily routine.

What might be a minor irritation to them in terms of building design and layout could prove to be unworkable for you.

1.3   GREEN FIELD SITE

This option has many long-term advantages over the purchase of existing premises, particularly if you want to develop a large complex of kennels.

A green field site gives you the option to construct modern, well-designed kennels, to your requirements. It also allows you to develop the site from scratch, to ensure that the buildings are in the correct position; it removes any restrictions that may occur with existing kennels.

The proposed development can be phased over a period of time to take into account restrictions on time and finances.

The down side of this option is:

- Locating a suitable site that is close to an area of habitation; but not too close as to result in complaints to the local authority i.e. noise and traffic.

- Satisfying the local authority in terms of planning.

- To develop a successful business can take a considerable amount of time; the interim period can be extremely difficult in financial terms.

- A time delay before any revenue starts to come in.

- Does the area have enough capacity to sustain another commercial or welfare centre?

1.4   PLANNING PERMISSION

As I have already mentioned, the first difficulty is in locating a suitable site; the second major obstacle is in obtaining permission either for a Green Field site or to develop an existing one. From past experience most local authorities put up their hands in horror when confronted with an application to develop kennels; whether this is for boarding, breeding or welfare work.

Most types of development require permission from the local authority; applications for permission are made to the district council unless the proposed development relates to a county matter when the application is made direct to the county council.

Planning applications are of two types, namely, *Outline* and *Full.*

An **Outline** application is normally made before a property is purchased and the applicant wishes to know whether the principle of the proposed development is acceptable to the local authority. At this stage the applicant will not normally have detailed plans of the proposed development, merely an overall plan of what is proposed; legally he/she is not required to give any more details than the location and a brief description of the proposal. However, it is good practice to include as much detail as possible, e.g. type and size of the proposed kennels, elevation drawings.

The more information you can give to the planning authority will help enable them to give you a more informed guide as to the suitability of your proposal. Such applications, if they are accepted in principle, will be approved subject to the subsequent satisfactory submission of details relating to the siting, design, external appearance, means of escape etc.

Once the local planning authority has given outline planning permission it is committed to the development.

The next stage is to obtain **Full** permission - this application contains all of the required information, which the authority will need in order to give their stamp of approval. Even at this stage it is open to the authority to request further information if they deem it necessary.

From past experience it is advisable to obtain the services of an expert, one who is familiar with the local council and who knows the topography. This is normally in the form of an architect, a surveyor or even a quality building contractor.

1.5   TIME LIMITS

Planning permissions are normally valid only for five years from the date of the permission being granted; although the authority may, in exceptional circumstances, substitute a period either longer or shorter.

In the case of Outline permissions, the submission of details must be made within three years of the date of the outline permission and the development must be commenced within two years from the date of approval of the details.

If a Full planning permission is not acted upon within the stated time limits, it lapses, and a new permission must be obtained.

1.6   PLANNING FEES

All applications for planning permission have to be accompanied with the relevant fee; the scale of fees being subject to regular increases. The amount of fee depends on the size and nature of the development, this ranges from £90 to over £14,000.

Obviously, the higher the fee the larger the scale of the development. *The planning application will not be valid unless it is accompanied with the correct fee.* There are a few, exceptional cases where no planning fee, or a reduced fee is payable, details can be obtained from the planning authority. In dealing with a planning application, local authorities can either:

- Approve it outright.
- Approve it subject to conditions.
- Refuse it.

An applicant, who receives a planning refusal or an approval with conditions and who objects to these, has the right, within a period of six months to appeal against the decision to the Secretary of State.

Clearly, if the correct approach has been carried out and sensible discussions have taken place with the planning authority and advice taken, any major obstacles will hopefully have been avoided.

The normal time scale for a decision to be made known is approximately 8 weeks

1.7   ENFORCEMENT OF PLANNING CONTROL

Local planning authorities have powers to ensure that any unauthorised development that has been carried out is rectified. Unauthorised development is not in itself an offence, the exception being listed buildings. Once the unlawful development comes to the notice of the authority it will decide what action is to be taken. This decision is taken upon the nature of the development, any local restrictions, materials used, etc.

There are two ways an infringement can occur: *firstly*, for a development that has been carried out without planning permission and *secondly*, for a development that has been granted permission, but has not complied with the specific conditions being imposed by the planning authority.

1.8   BUILDING REGULATIONS

Building Regulations are totally separate to planning permission. Although Building Control may be housed in the same building as the planning authority; they are two self-governing bodies; totally independent of each other. Under normal circumstances all schemes require Building Regulation approval. However, it is worth checking with the Building Control officer to establish if all of your proposed development will require permission.

What is Building Control?

The Building Regulations, made under the Building Act of 1984, require that buildings which are erected, extended, altered or which have a material change in their use, are capable of performing to *minimum* standards.

These standards are set to protect the health, safety and welfare of people; to conserve energy and to prevent contamination of land and water. To ensure that these standards are met requires that you inform the Building Control office of your intentions.

Your architect or surveyor will normally address the specific technical requirements of the Regulations; however, there is no reason to stop you from dealing with the department yourself. If you decide to tackle this issue yourself it will be worthwhile purchasing a copy of the basic technical manual, Schedule 1 of the Building Regulations 1991.

<u>The approved documents within the schedule are broken down into the following sections:</u>

- **Approved Document A - Structure** this gives guidance about ways of meeting the requirements of the Regulations to ensure the structural stability of buildings.

- **Approved Document B - Fire Safety** shows ways of ensuring that buildings have adequate means of escape in case of fire, that the internal spread of fire through its linings and structure and the external spread is limited and that access and facilities are provided for the Fire Service.

- **Approved Document C - Site Preparation and Resistance to Moisture** advises about ways of fulfilling the requirements for site preparation, dealing with dangerous and offensive substances, subsoil drainage and resistance to weather and ground moisture.

- **Approved Document D - Toxic Substances** gives guidance about the materials to be used to insulate cavity walls.

- **Approved Document E - Resistance to the Passage of Sound** contains guidance about insulation against airborne and impact sound.

- **Approved Document F – Ventilation** advises about fulfilling the requirements for adequate means of ventilation in buildings and the control of condensation in roofs.

- **Approved Document G - Hygiene** gives help about fulfilling the requirements which relate to the provision of sanitary conveniences, washing facilities, bathrooms and hot water storage.

- **Approved Document H - Drainage and waste disposal** gives guidance about pipework and drainage provision, including cesspools and tanks, rainwater drainage and solid waste storage.

- **Approved Document J - Heat producing appliances** contains guidance about the requirements relating to the installation of heat producing appliances.

- **Approved Document K - Stairs, ramps and guards** provides guidance about stairs, ramps, protection against falling and vehicle barriers.

- **Approved Document L - Conservation of Fuel and Power** gives guidance how to conserve energy.

- **Approved Document M - Access and facilities for disabled people** gives guidance about the access to and use of the building, the provision of satisfactory sanitary conveniences and the provision of suitable audience and spectator seating.

- **Approved document N - Glazing, materials and protection** provides guidance about glazing materials, the protection of glazed openings and requirements relating to visual awareness.

The Regulations recognise that certain small buildings or buildings put to certain uses, are adequately controlled by other legislation can be exempted.

<u>The 7 classes of building in Schedule 2 which are exempt from Building Control are:</u>

- **Class 1** - Buildings Controlled Under Other Legislation - i.e. Nuclear Power Plants, Explosives stores and factories, Ancient Monuments and Architectural Areas.
- **Class 11** - Buildings Not Frequented by People - i.e. Detached buildings into which people do not normally go, e.g. plant and machinery rooms.
- **Class 111** - Greenhouses and Agricultural Buildings - These include most buildings used to house non-domestic livestock, i.e. cattle sheds, poultry houses and greenhouses used for the production of growing seeds/plants, etc.
- **Class 1V** - Temporary Buildings - Buildings where the use is to be for 28 days or less i.e. caravans, exhibition trailers.
- **Class V** - Ancillary Buildings - Buildings used on a construction site or mine. They must not contain any form of sleeping quarters.
- **Class V1** - Small Detached Buildings - i.e. detached buildings not used for sleeping accommodation with a floor area not exceeding $30m^2$ e.g. garages, sheds, rest rooms.
- **Class V11** - Extensions - An extension at ground floor level of a conservatory, porch or covered yard.

The above classes and the extent of limitations are not exhaustive, merely indicative of the seven classes used by the local authority. Once again, it is extremely worthwhile discussing your proposal with the local officers; do not be misled into thinking that they are against you and do not want the proposal to commence, they are merely doing their job to ensure that you comply with the Regulations.

1.9 BUILDING NOTICE

A person who intends to carry out building work or to make a material change of use must give a Building Notice to the local authority; failure to do so is a contravention of the Regulations and is subject to a fine.

The person responsible for giving the required Notice is usually the builder, as he/she is more up to date with developments than most. Once full plans or Building Notice has been submitted you may start work. It is at this stage that further details may be asked for i.e. structural calculations for steelwork or disabled access.

The Building Inspector will consult with the fire authority; a copy of your plans will go to the fire officer for his/her comments regarding your proposal. They have the right to ensure that the building comes up to the required regulations, in terms of fire safety and access.

1.10 BUILDING CONTROL INSPECTION PROCESS

The Building Inspector will visit the site through key stages of the development. The aim of these inspections is to ensure that the technical requirements of the Regulations are being adhered to.

Fees

The Building Regulations 1994 require the local authorities to charge a fee in accordance with a fixed scale of charges. The developer or client normally pays the cost of this charge.

The two main fees are:

- A plan fee paid when the plans are deposited. Again, as with planning applications, unless the correct fee is paid the plans will not be valid.
- An inspection fee, payable on demand and made after the inspector has carried out the first inspection.

SCALE OF CHARGES

Total estimated cost of work.	Plan fee	Inspection fee	Building Notice fee	Regularisation fee
up to £2000	£60	-	£60	£72
£2000 - £5000	£150	-	£150	£180
£5000 - £20,000	25% of building notice fee	75% of building notice fee	£150 + £10 for every £1000 over £5000	120% of notice fee. "
£20,000-£100,000	"	"	£300 + £8 for every £1000 over £20,000	

The scale of charges continues to rise with increments of £100,000 to £1 million, £1 million to £10 million and over £10 million.

1.11 CONSTRUCTION (DESIGN & MANAGEMENT) REGULATIONS 1994

The CDM Regulations came into full operation in March 1995. The aim of the CDM Regulations is to promote better safety standards and health and safety provisions for construction workers. The responsibility for enforcing CDM Regulations lies with the Health and Safety Executive.

The CDM Regulations place specific duties on all parties involved with the development, i.e. client, design professionals, contractors and subcontractors.

Client

The client is the person or persons responsible for ordering the construction work on a building and who pays for that work. The client is normally the owner, but could be the manager or leaseholder.

The specific requirements of the client placed on him/her by the CDM Regulations are:

- To ensure that there are sufficient resources to complete the project, i.e. time and money.
- To make all site information available to the design team.
- To appoint a competent principal contractor.
- To appoint a planning supervisor and a competent designer.
- To ensure that no construction work commences until a health and safety plan has been agreed.

Planning supervisor

This appointment is a new requirement under the CDM Regulations. The function is very close to that of project manager.

The main duties are:
- To ensure a competent person addresses all health and safety matters during the design stage.
- To ensure that a safety plan is produced.
- To advise the client and contractor on all health and safety issues.
- To inform the Health and Safety Executive on the development of the project.

- Any member of the design team, or an independent organisation can perform the role of planning supervisor; however, it must be a specific appointment. Consideration, as with all professions, should be given to ensure that the appointee has suitable professional indemnity insurance.

Designer

A designer is anyone who has an input to the design or preparation of the specification. A designer must demonstrate that he/she has given consideration to all health and safety issues relevant to the construction works.

The responsibilities of the designer do not end with the completion of the contract. The CDM Regulations state that the designer has an ongoing responsibility for the building. This responsibility will include such items as consideration for future maintenance, materials and eventual demolition.

Main contractor

The main or principal contractor has a duty under the CDM Regulation to comply with sections of them. The main duties are to produce a health and safety plan and suitable methods of working for the contract. They will be expected to supervise all contractors/subcontractors in relation to this plan.

Project Progress

The HSE must be notified for all contracts that fall under the CDM Regulations, this notification is normally issued by the planning supervisor at the commitment stage.

The details required are:

- The site address.
- The client's particulars.
- Project type.
- Planning supervisor details.
- Main contractor.
- Date of commencement.
- Estimated duration of the contract.
- The number of contractors on the site.

1.12 SIMPLIFIED PROGRESS CHART FOR NEW BUILD/ MAJOR REFURBISHMENT WORKS

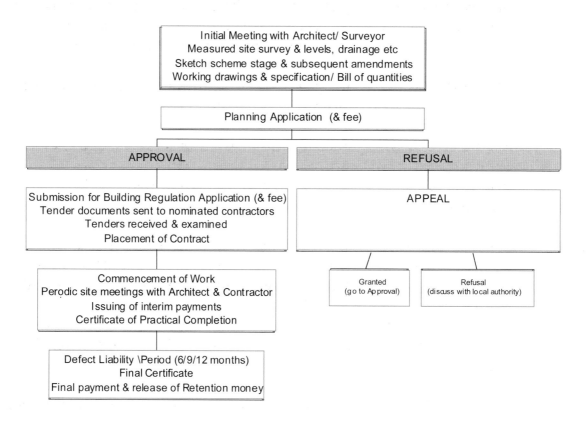

Guidance Notes for Larger Contracts

- At the initial meeting with the Architect the general principles of the scheme will be discussed, any cost restraints discussed and a fee agreed. The fee can either be a fixed amount; this is more normal for smaller contracts, or a percentage of the total contract sum. It is normal for an architect/surveyor to outline the stage payments required and other services that are not included in his/her fee i.e. structural engineer. If you have thought about what you want from the buildings, layout etc it can be a major saving in time and money.

- Alterations can be made at any time, but it is good policy to have ironed out all revisions before work commences.

- Where refurbishment work is undertaken there can be a significant disruption of services, these areas should have been addressed during the early discussions with the architect; indeed to comply with CDM Regulations all aspects of the project will need to be taken into account. It might be necessary to provide temporary services i.e. water, electricity, however all of these have a cost implication.

- The Contract document will comprise of working drawings, a specification/ Bill of Quantities, a Health & Safety plan and the signed Contract.

- Site meetings are normally on a monthly basis, however they can be as often or as few as required. Normal practice is for all amendments and alterations to be issued by the Architect, direct to the contractor. This avoids confusion and keeps costs in order.

- Larger contracts are paid on a monthly basis; the Architect issues interim certificates, after consultation with the supervising officer or quantity surveyor. The certificates represent the value of the work completed to date. It is normal practice for a retention of 5% to be withheld at this stage.

- At the end of the contract; the practical completion, 2.5% of the retention with be paid

- At the expiration of the Defects Liability Period, the contractor will have rectified any defective items. It is at this stage that the final certificate is issued; and all monies released.

Project Development Costs

Clearly, before you embark upon a project you will need to know what the final cost is going to be. It is not uncommon for the peripheral items to be overlooked or indeed some of the more general items such as connection to the mains sewage system.

Some local authorities charge on a per-building scale and some on site rate; this can make a significant difference.

The following list shows some of the main items that should be taken into account when preparing your budget for any new development. Clearly this is not exhaustive but is merely indicative of the different areas/items that should be taken into account.

SAMPLE PROJECT DEVELOPMENT COST-SHEET

FEES	£	EXTERNAL WORKS	£
Planning Permission		Car park	
Building Regulations.		Lighting	
Architect		Landscaping	
Quantity Surveyor		Fencing	
Structural Engineer		Road signage	
Mechanical/electrical Engineer		Sound bunding	
Land Agent		Landscaping	
Land Surveyor		Sub-total	
CDM Planning Officer			
Infrastructure costs -		**EQUIPMENT**	
Electricity -		Laundry equipment	
Gas -		Pressure washer/steam cleaner	
Water -		Water hose/fittings	
Drainage -		Fire prevention	
Specialist Contractors i.e. Asbestos removal		Office/staff room furniture + fittings	
New buildings		Computer	
Sub-total		Telephones + intercom	
TEMPORARY WORKS		Kennel furniture i.e. beds bowls	
Fencing/security		Music system	
Accommodation		Safe/security box	
Services i.e. gas		Vehicle	
Sub-total		Grooming/dog bath	
MAIN BUILDINGS		Sub-total	
Reception			
Kennels			
Isolation			
		PROJECT TOTAL	
Sub-total			

1.13 DEMOLITION

It may be necessary to demolish existing buildings on a newly acquired site. The reasons for this are to clear part of the site for future development, to remove or make safe any structures in an unsafe condition.

The law regarding demolition is very specific and should not be taken lightly, with statutory requirements that must be adhered to. For any large-scale demolition, expert advice should normally be sought.

Generally, consent to demolish a building is not required under the Town and Country Planning Acts, the exception to this being for a listed building. However, a person intending to demolish a building or part of it must give notice under section 80 of the Building Act 1984 to the local authority.

The Building Control section of the local authority usually undertakes the control of such work. The notice usually takes the form of a letter describing the impending work and a site plan showing the location and the building.

In addition to the authority the owner or his/her agent must also notify –

- Any utility boards i.e. gas, electricity.
- The owner/occupiers of any building adjacent to the building concerned.

1.14 TREE PRESERVATION ORDERS

Law regards trees as permanent assets attached to the property/land; therefore, they cannot be felled, removed or topped without permission. This relates to "timber-like trees" only and not ornamental shrubs or bushes.

Owners of trees are responsible for ensuring that any tree on their property is in a safe and sound condition and does not obstruct public rights of way or highways.

If the land surrounding your property is designated a conservation area by the local authority, six weeks' notification is required before any work can be carried out on a tree. This period allows the authority the opportunity to make a decision whether a preservation order is required for the tree in question.

COMMON ERRORS WHICH ARE COSTLY & SHOULD BE AVOIDED

- Lack of forward planning. Plan well ahead and try to foresee how your business will grow and expand. Allow for this, do not sterilise a site by poor planning.

- Single storey buildings constructed with insufficient foundations for adding a second storey, this is particularly relevant if space is limited and the only way for expansion is to build upwards rather than outwards.

- Piecemeal building instead of a planned integrated unit. This is where having a professional site survey carried out is extremely beneficial.

- Inadequate car parking.

- Inadequate storage facility.

- If converting a site, do not allow existing structures to stop the correct siting of new buildings/facilities.

- Lack of quiet areas.

- Poor quality finishes i.e. floor/wall.

- Poor location of various facilities in relation to other units.

- Lack of acoustic control measures.

- Not providing separate public and staff zones.

Above all - have a clear idea of what you want from the business/centre, research the project thoroughly, visit similar units, most owners/managers are only too willing to spend time with you to discuss their site; both strong and weak areas of it.

MAKE YOUR MISTAKES ON PAPER – NOT DURING THE BUILDING STAGE!

2.1   SITE LAYOUT

The layout and design for your site will depend on many restraints i.e. space, finances and any existing buildings that can be used.
The layout should encompass some very basic design rules that are applicable to all kennels.

These are:

- Security.

- Ease of access for loading/unloading.

- Adequate car parking.

- Suitable areas for future expansion.

- Suitable storage facilities and ancillary buildings close to the main centre of operation.

- A pleasing, professional appearance, this can be achieved using suitable colours and materials and professionally landscaped areas.

- External exercising areas.

SEE FIGURES 1 & 2 FOR A TYPICAL LAYOUTS

Typical Site Layout (Small)

Drawings courtesy of
FORUM ARCHITECTS

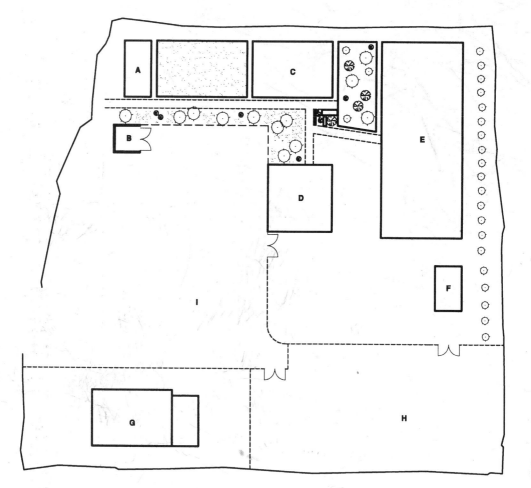

A - Isolation
B - Refuse Area
C - Cattery
D - Reception Building
E - Kennel unit (32) with central kitchen, laundry
F - Bulk Store
G - Residential Accommodation
H - Grass exercise area

Typical Site Layout (Large)

Drawings courtesy of
FORUM ARCHITECTS

A - Isolation
B - Store
C - Refuse Area
D - Cattery
E - Service Road
F - Residential Accommodation
G - Garage
H - Reception
I - Kennels x 20
J - Kennels x 20
K - Grass Exercise Run
L - Grass Exercise Run

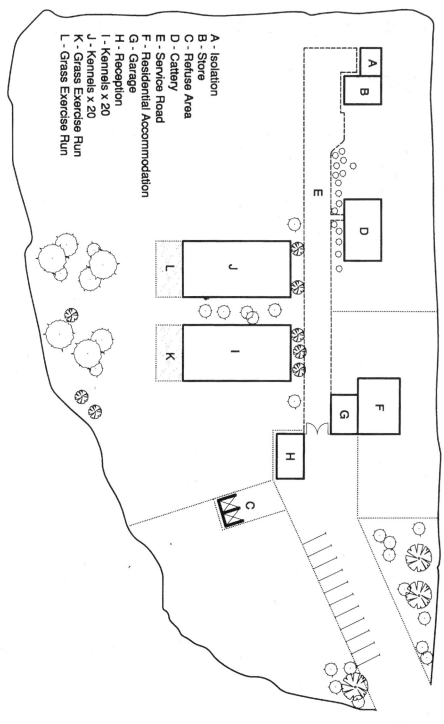

2.2   ASPECT

In an ideal world all of the buildings will face South/ Southwest. This means that the exercise runs catch the sun, helping to dry them out more quickly than if they were facing to the North. This arrangement also means that the animals benefit from the warmth of the sun.

Clearly, it is not always possible to ensure that all of the buildings face to the South, however, it is worth ensuring that some do. Again, this comes back to the site and design being flexible; if it is in a boarding establishment, where only some of the kennels are used during the winter months, ideally, these should be the kennels that are used.

2.3   RECEPTION

This is normally the first building that most clients/customers will go to. This building is extremely important, not only does it function as an office, shop etc it is the first impression of the property that most people will have.

The design and size can be as elaborate and spacious or as simple as you require.

<u>In order to highlight how flexible and versatile this building can be I have listed other uses for it -</u>

- Reception counter/desk - You will need an area where the public can fill out documents, sign cheques, etc. The installation of electrical sockets is a normal requirement for calculators, cash tills and computers.

- Manager's office - This is often a dual-purpose room, not only serving as a quiet area in which to retire to concentrate on office paperwork, accounts, etc. It also offers a suitable room away from the main building to discuss private matters with owners and staff.

- Sales area - The installation of a sales area is common practice for boarding kennels and welfare centres; it can provide an easy form of additional income. The sales goods can be basic items like toys and dog chews through to bulk sales of dog food.

- Staff accommodation - Do you require staff to live on site? If so, how many? The building of accommodation above the reception can serve a dual role: it utilises space, it provides additional security for the site and is a cost-effective method of providing accommodation. One disadvantage to this is that the staff are always above a source of activity, even on their days off.

- Public toilet - The provision of a public toilet is only common sense. It is normally a planning requirement to install a disabled toilet.

- Staff room - With heating, washing facilities, hot/cold water, fridge, microwave and soft furnishings. It can be of great benefit for staff to get together over coffee to chat and discuss the centres activities.

- Shower - A showering facility is becoming a standard fitting for large charities. It shows a positive attitude to Health & Safety.

- Staff toilet - It is always preferable to try and install separate toilets for staff and clients.

- Holding room for dogs that are being discharged - This can be part of the veterinary inspection room if required. The purpose of this room is to provide a clean, quiet area away from the main kennel building, this gives the opportunity to hold dogs if an owner is going to turn up late, or if the dog has been bathed and is waiting for collection.

- Veterinary inspection room - This can be part of the main reception building, it can also be incorporated within the main kennel buildings. The advantage of keeping it away from the main kennels is that there will be less distraction for the animal being examined by the vet, it will also be quieter.

- Boiler room - This depends on the system and its sophistication.

- Public telephone - This removes the continual request to use your telephone.

- Storage room - Again, an often-overlooked area.

SEE FIGURES THREE AND FOUR FOR A TYPICAL LAYOUTS

Typical Reception Layout (small)

Drawings courtesy of
FORUM ARCHITECTS

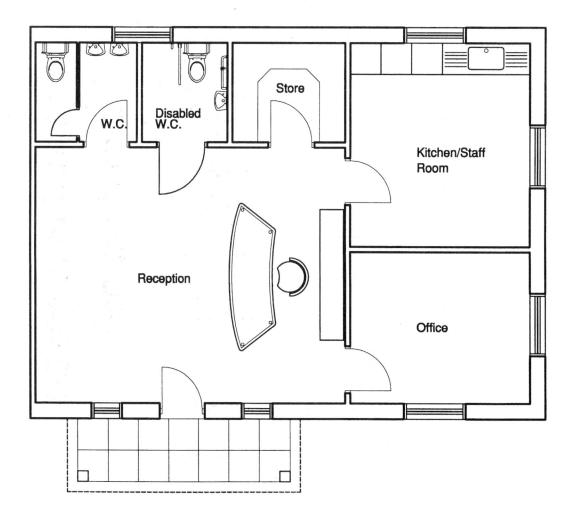

Typical Reception
Layout (large)

Drawings courtesy of
FORUM ARCHITECTS

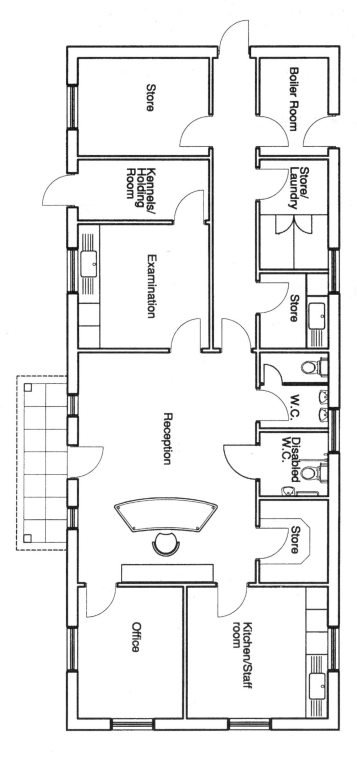

Boiler Room

Store

Kennels/
Holding
Room

Store/
Laundry

Examination

Store

W.C.

Reception

Disabled
W.C.

Store

Office

Kitchen/Staff
room

2.4   ISOLATION

All animal establishments should have an isolation facility in order to contain and prevent the spread of infectious diseases.

<u>The Chartered Institute of Environmental Health (CIEH) insist on the following requirement:</u>
- One isolation kennel for up to fifty kennels and pro-rata above that
- A minimum separation of 5m from any other animal units in existing facilities and 10m for newly constructed kennels.

Due to the limited use most isolation kennels receive, it has been a normal practice to construct them to a lesser standard than the main kennels. Thought should be given to ensure that these kennels are of an equal standard, if not higher than the main units.

The reasoning behind this is simple; an isolation kennel needs to be thoroughly cleaned and disinfected after each use in order to prevent any cross contamination to future users. The cleaning process may involve the use of mist spraying, steam cleaning or chemical means, the construction should take these issues into account.

It is always a contentious point; how many isolation kennels should you have. The CIEH have given their recommendations, however, I would argue that these are not sufficient and should be increased. In an ideal world I would recommend two separate buildings with two/three kennels to each. Again, the reasons are simple, there is no point in putting a dog that is simply 'looking off colour' into the isolation building with a dog that is obviously ill and under veterinary treatment.

It is far better to adopt a flexible approach with more buildings, this enables you to segregate the animals and hopefully, prevent any cross infection. Obviously, if you have a major outbreak of a virus/disease, which has infected a large percentage of the animals in your care, a few isolation kennels will be totally inadequate. Hopefully, these problems can be minimized and better isolated with improved kennel design as suggested later in the book.

Clearly the isolation facility should be totally self-contained with its own hot water supply, protective clothing, food supplies, food bowls and cleaning utensils. Ideally, the person responsible for this unit should not be working with healthy animals. If this is not possible then high standards of 'barrier nursing' should be employed, with the use of washable PVC coveralls, wellingtons and disposable gloves. All of these measures will create additional work; they are not always guaranteed to be 100% effective, however without them the problems will be much worse.

SEE FIGURE FIVE FOR A TYPICAL DESIGN

Suggested Layout for an Isolation Kennel

Drawings courtesy of
FORUM ARCHITECTS

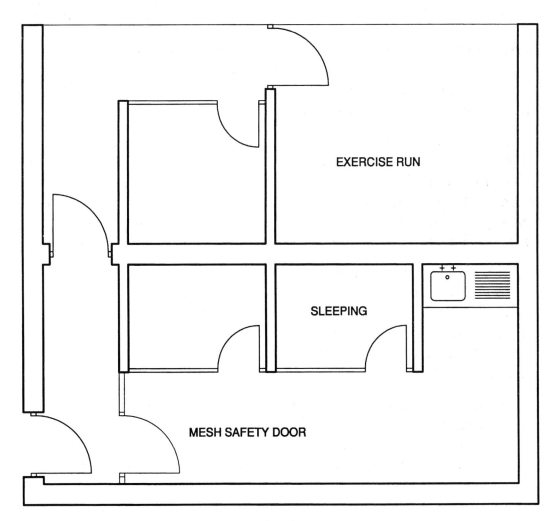

EXERCISE RUN

SLEEPING

MESH SAFETY DOOR

2.5 ADMISSIONS UNIT

The installation of an admissions unit is not a new concept; however they have gained popularity particularly with sanctuaries and welfare centres. The idea is to use the buildings as a form of 'pre-isolation' prior to admitting the dogs into the main kennel blocks.

The aim of the unit is to minimize the risk of an outbreak of disease in the main building, thus preventing the temporary closure of the homing kennels. They have a clear and defined use for welfare centres and sanctuaries, which may have to admit dogs from unknown backgrounds and keep them for several weeks. Their use for boarding kennel owners may be somewhat limited, as the average stay is 1-3 weeks.

Like an isolation unit it should be totally self-contained i.e. hot water, utensils and if possible, staff. Obviously the number of kennels required is dependent on the total number of animals coming into your care. If the average monthly figure for dogs being rehomed is sixty, then the number of admission kennels will require to be approximately thirty, this taking into account that the dogs will be in this unit for fourteen days.

Obviously the charity/owner has to take into account several factors before such a unit is constructed, these being:

- The cost implication to construct these kennels
- Planning and space restrictions
- Time considerations - How long will the dogs be kept in this building, type of animals coming into your care, do they have a documented background and are they vaccinated?
- If you have to close down, what happens to the dogs on your waiting list? Is there an alternative sanctuary/centre for them to go to?
- Financial - Can you afford to keep the dogs for an extended period of time.

2.6 ZONING

Clearly you do not want the public to have free access to the site, unless under supervision. In order to be aware who is on the premises, the design must funnel all clients/customers through a barrier system. Not only does this prevent unwanted visitors, it also secures the site and minimises the chance of an animal escaping. This is illustrated in the typical design layouts.

2.7 CAR PARKING

Larger kennels/welfare centres have designated parking for staff and for the public. Thought must be given to the number of staff that is likely to be employed and the availability of public transport. If the site is isolated and staff have no other way of getting to it, except by their own car, adequate parking must be made available.

The number of spaces required for the public is often difficult to estimate; as a general guide I would suggest parking for a minimum of six vehicles. Some council have adopted the Planning Information Policy Paper, No 11. This gives guidance for various activities, i.e. residential, hotels, retail, etc. The closest category for kennels/catteries is veterinary establishments.

The recommendations for these are:
>   1 space per vet plus 2 spaces per vet for patients
>   1 space per professional staff
>   1 space per 3 non-professional staff.

The space required for various types of vehicles is as shown:

VEHICLE TYPE	LENGTH	WIDTH	TURNING CIRCLE
Small car	3.05m	1.41m	8.60m
Medium family car	4.47m	1.71m	10.46m
Large saloon car	5.35m	1.90m	12.70m
Van (1 tonne)	4.40m	1.78m	12.20m
Van (2 tonne)	6.00m	2.24m	13.10m
Dustcart (10.8 tonnes)	7.40m	2.29m	14.00m
Fire appliance (8.3 tonnes)	8.00m	2.29m	15.20m
3 axle skip lorry	7.00m	2.50m	17.40m
Ridged lorry (16.2 tonnes)	8.50m	2.50m	21.00m
Articulated lorry (38 tonnes)	15.00m	2.50m	12.00 –15.00m

2.8   LAUNDRY

The issue of laundry equipment, type of bedding to be used and infrastructure services should be addressed at the outset of the development; it should be considered as an integral part of the project.

The problems associated with cleaning animal bedding can be a major source of irritation, expenditure, time and energy to the kennel owner who has not addressed this issue. The normal end result being unsatisfactory arrangements that, in the long term, are often more costly. Correctly addressed, this problem becomes just another part of normal day to day activities leaving you concentrate on the more important issues. The installation of suitably sized laundry equipment is essential for any modern animal establishment using fabric bedding. The provision of a laundry will depend on the type of bedding that is used.

The options available are:

- Proprietary vet bedding.
- Old blankets/sheets.
- Shredded newspaper/computer paper.

Which option used is a matter of personal choice, availability and cost. From a practical and personal point of view I have to recommend the proprietary vet bedding. It is light, hygienic, easy to wash, dries very quickly, provides high levels of comfort for the dog and is aesthetically pleasing; the disadvantage is the high initial cost.

The use of old blankets/sheets is a close substitute; it is surprising how easy it is to obtain old bedding free of charge. The disadvantage over vet type bedding is that larger pieces are required to provide the same level of padding and comfort and it takes considerably longer to dry. This can be a major problem when faced with a large quantity of washing! *Remember that any establishment with over 40 dogs generates a considerable amount of washing on a daily basis!*

The use of shredded news/computer paper can be a cheap alternative. This can either be shredded on site with a suitable machine or purchased in pre-shredded bales. The disadvantage of using newspaper is that the print comes off the paper when it is wet; this can look very unsightly in the kennel and can also mark the animal's coat.

Computer paper is a better alternative and has the advantage over newspaper in that the print does not come off so readily.

Large quantities are required to provide a sufficient level of padding and comfort for the animal. The other consideration when using this material is the question of disposal.

Remember that a large percentage of this paper will be wet and therefore will not burn readily.

If you opt for material bedding you will need a suitable washing machine/s to cope with the loads being generated on a daily basis. A normal domestic machine is not adequate and will not be able to cope for a prolonged period of time. The only answer is to install a commercial machine/s; I would suggest that the minimum size should be approximately 18lb (8 kg). Ideally, the larger machine that you have space for and can afford the better; a machine with a capacity of approximately 25-50lb (11.3-22kg) will provide a cost effective, reliable, long term solution.

Generally, the preferred option for larger charities is to install one central laundry room for the entire site. This option allows for the installation of single, larger machines which pro-rata is cheaper than smaller, individual units. The down side of this option is that it does not offer any flexibility if a machine breaks down. However, with a reliable company that provides a good breakdown service this should not be a major problem.

The other option is to install smaller machines into each kennel block. Clearly this system ensures that you will always have at least one machine working at any one time. The decision is down to personal choice, site layout, building design and size.

To be able to clean the bedding is one thing; the next problem is trying to dry it. Remember that you cannot always rely on drying the bedding naturally; the British weather is too unreliable! Therefore, you are going to need some method, which will allow fast, effective drying. Clearly, the simplest solution is to install a suitably sized tumble dryer to match the washing machine. It is pointless having a large commercial washing machine and only a domestic tumble dryer.

In order to make full use of the washing machine an equivalent sized tumble dryer needs to be installed. Generally, it is accepted that the dryer needs to be slightly larger than the washing machine.

In order for the larger commercial machines to operate effectively they normally require a three-phase electricity supply for the washing machine and a gas supply for the tumble dryer. A pre-heated supply of hot water will reduce the running costs and help speed up the wash cycle. All of the larger tumble dryers are normally heated by gas; the use of electrically heated dryers is prohibitively expensive.

Although this equipment is not cheap to purchase, there are several options available to the kennel owner. The commercial machines are sometimes sold off from launderettes and hospitals or can be purchased from the specialist auctions advertised around the country. The down side with this form of procurement is the uncertain service history, lack of installation information etc. A far better option is to contact one of the specialist manufacturers/ suppliers such as John Laithwaite Associates Ltd.

Being one of the largest companies in the country; they are responsible for supplying laundry equipment to the prison service, launderettes and hospitals, etc. They offer a range of machines suitable for all requirements with a comprehensive back up service. They also have a leasing scheme for a wide range of their equipment. This option allows you the flexibility to ensure that you get the correct machines for your requirements, without the capital costs associated with outright purchase.

Helpful Hints –

📖 Ensure that the entrance door is at least 1000mm wide, this will allow the installation of the larger machines without having to remove doorframes etc. The normal width for an entrance door is 838mm. One way to overcome this is to either have a purpose made door installed or a cheaper option is to use a solid core door blank. These blanks come in widths up to 1200mm.

📖 Try to ensure that the laundry area has at least one external wall, this will allow the tumble dryer flue to be directly vented to the outside. This gives the most cost-effective installation and improves the efficiency of the machine.

📖 Install a floor drain outlet within the laundry area, this will allow any water to drain away from wet bedding or floods etc.

📖 A solid, concrete floor is needed for all commercial machines.

📖 Do not try to mix the laundry area with the boiler room, blanket fluff and boilers are not compatible.

LAUNDRY EQUIPMENT GUIDE

MACHINE	SIZE	WEIGHT	SUPPLY	COST – GUIDE ONLY
Maytag tumble dryer - gas/electric 8 kg load	H – 1070mm W - 683mm D - 711mm	70kgs	240v 1ph	£850.00
Maytag washer 7 kg load - cold fill	As above	70kgs	240v 1ph	£1000.00
Ipso HW64 - washer/extractor - High speed spin (6.5kg load)	H - 1005mm W - 660mm D - 670mm	197kg	415v 3ph	£2200.00
Ipso HW131 - washer/extractor - High speed spin (13.2 kg load)	H - 1170mm W - 780mm D - 760mm	287kg	415v 3ph	£3700.00
ADC tumble dryer - Gas heated (11.5 kg load)	H - 1829mm W - 870mm D - 756mm	199kg	240V 1ph	£1600.00
ADC tumble dryer - Gas heated (23kg)	H - 1829mm W - 870mm D - 1283mm	307kg	240V 1ph	£2400.00

2.9   STORAGE FACILITY

This is another area that is much underestimated. The problem of not providing suitable and adequate storage can be extremely tiresome.

Ideally, this facility should be large enough to provide dry, vermin-free storage for the entire site; be close to the working area and have suitable access for vehicular and pedestrian traffic.

The building will need to have a range of suitable racking to help make full use of it. This is normally in the form of purpose designed warehouse type systems, floor pallets or secure bins with lockable lids.

Another important aspect to consider is the off loading of deliveries and moving of supplies once on the site. Apart from the time factor, the Health and Safety of staff has to be considered.

It is worth going to farm auctions, government surplus sales, etc to try and purchase suitable equipment to move supplies around the site; it is far cheaper than buying new.

2.10 REFUSE AREA

This is yet another area that tends to get overlooked, often resulting in inadequate provision, with dustbins being left all around the site, creating a poor impression; all due to lack of forward planning. However, before an area is dedicated, thought should be given to establish what method of collection is available for the disposal of the waste generated. The most common systems used are:

- Plastic bags.
- Standard council plastic wheeled bins – Capacity from 90-330 litres
- Small skip type wheeled bins – Capacity from 500-1100 litres.
- Open/covered skips, delivered/collected by purpose built vehicles, the capacities are 2000-16000 litres.

Before a contract is placed with any supplier, questions that need to be clarified are:

- What is the most suitable arrangement for you?

- How much waste will be generated? This will determine the size of the area to be provided, *(as a general guide an establishment with around forty kennels and thirty cat units will generate approximately 2000 -3000 litres per week).*

- Is the area accessible for the proposed collection vehicle, see section on vehicle sizes?

- Can the area be isolated and screened off from the main buildings and public?

- Is the area accessible for the operators during unsocial hours, without disturbing the animals or staff?

- What type of surface is available? Are there any steps or ramps? It can be extremely difficult manoeuvring a full 1100 litre down steps or over gravel and soil.

- How frequent is the collection service?

- If plastic bags are going to be used, some form of caging may be required to prevent dogs/foxes from damaging the bags.

2.11 INCINERATOR

Whilst the installation of an incinerator might seem a cost-effective solution to removing a large percentage of the waste generated on the site, beware, it has hidden costs and legal requirements and may prove to be more problematical than first envisaged. Incinerators come in many guises, sizes and levels of efficiency; they all aim to achieve the same end result, to transform the waste into a less hazardous, less bulky or more controllable form.

The problem with most waste generated from kennels is that is tends to be metal from cans of food, waste products that have been soiled with faeces/urine and faecal matter. All of these present their own difficulties, the former is not suitable for incineration in small domestic units, while the latter is classed as clinical waste and comes under strict legislation and control.

Most, but not all, local authorities deem animal faeces and materials contaminated with faecal matter as clinical waste and are therefore not suitable for collection under normal refuse systems.

If you intend to install any form of incinerator, please ensure that you contact the local authority to establish what the current legislation is and what permissions are required.

The legal definition for clinical waste is given in the Controlled Waste Regulations 1992 as:

" any waste which consists wholly or partly of animal or human tissue, blood or other body fluids, excretions, drugs or other pharmaceutical products, swabs or dressings, or syringes, needles or other sharp instruments, being waste which unless rendered safe may prove hazardous to any person coming in contact with it; and any other waste arising from medical, nursing, dental, veterinary, pharmaceutical or similar practice, investigation, treatment, care, teaching or research, or the collection of blood for transfusion, being waste which may cause infection to any person coming in contact with it "

The basic designs for incinerators are:

- Open burning/smouldering - this is only suitable for burning clean, dry materials such as timber, paper, etc.

- Non- fuelled prefabricated systems - these are generally simple metal boxes with regulators and flues. These are most useful for burning general waste in a more controlled form than the above.

- Fuelled prefabricated units - these tend to be specialist systems for the incineration of specific waste and are designed for that purpose. This type of system is used in hospitals, research establishments, quarantine kennels and other secure operations.

At the time of writing, I have been quoted the following costs to install a small, non-fuelled system for the incineration of shavings from cat trays and general paper based waste:

ENVIRONMENTAL AGENCY - Waste Management Licence - Cost £1,000
LOCAL AUTHORITY - Annual inspection fee of £650.00

Clearly, with the cost of the incinerator, (approximately £2500.00) and the legal costs, it starts to become expensive.

2.12   DISABLED TOILET

As I have already mentioned, the provision of a disabled toilet is going to be a requirement imposed by the local authority when granting Planning Permission.

SEE FIGURE SIX FOR A TYPICAL INSTALLATION

Disabled W.C. Facility

Drawings courtesy of
FORUM ARCHITECTS

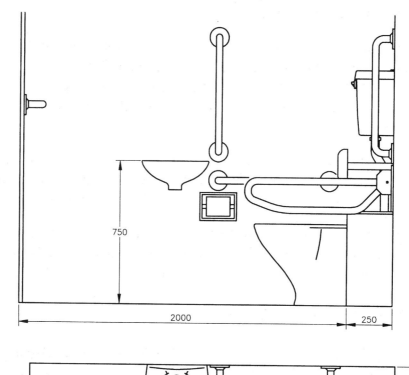

750

2000

250

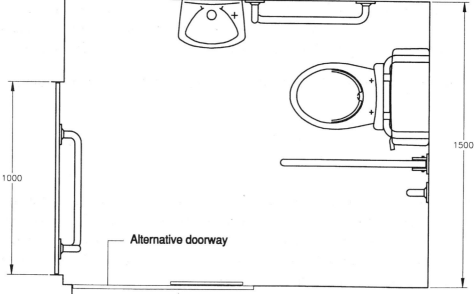

1000

1500

Alternative doorway

3.1 ARCHITECTURE

The construction style and choice of materials for the proposed development will depend on several issues; the location, the position of the site e.g. on top of a hill, areas with restricted planning. All locations pose their own difficulties and restrictions, some more onerous than others. The vernacular architecture can be broadly divided into domestic, agricultural and industrial; generally we will only be interested in domestic and agricultural.

The local planning authority will insist that any new development be designed in such a way as to be sympathetic to the style for that locality. All of these issues will need to be discussed with the Planning Authority at an early stage. It is pointless having plans drawn up for the development that will be totally unacceptable to the planners.

The normal choice for kennel construction materials is concrete block or brick. However in areas of natural outstanding beauty or restricted planning, the choice might be very limited, resulting in higher costs for the development.

Although kennels by their very nature can be very utilitarian, it is surprising how these buildings can be transformed and aesthetically improved with the correct choice of materials, colours and subtle architectural detail.

3.2 THERMAL INSULATION

The increasing demand to conserve fuel and reduce heating bills has led to greater levels of insulation in buildings; this applies to all buildings from domestic to industrial. In order to provide adequate levels of thermal comfort it is accepted that walls, floors and roofs should provide resistance to excessive transfer of heat.

The Building Regulations set maximum thermal resistance values for dwellings. These are:
- Walls = $0.60 \text{ W/m}^2 \text{ }^\circ\text{C}$
- Floors = $0.60 \text{ W/m}^2 \text{ }^\circ\text{C}$
- Roofs = $0.35 \text{ W/m}^2 \text{ }^\circ\text{C}$

- Thermal Transmittance is the rate at which heat is transferred through an element of a building and is called the thermal resistance or U - value. The lower the U - value, the better is the insulation and the lower the heat loss. U - values are expressed in $\text{W/m}^2 \text{ K}$ (watts per square metre for 1° C difference between internal and external temperatures)

Helpful Hints -

📖 It is worth checking with Building Control to establish if any of the new buildings will be exempt from Building Regulations. The interpretation of the regulations varies with each local authority. From experience this 'grey-area' applies to new buildings that are purely kennels and do not contain any form of habitable rooms for humans, i.e. staff rooms or kitchens. This point is worth considering, particularly if you own boarding kennels; as this 'grey-area' could reduce your building costs considerably by removing the inspection fees.

Walls – It is assumed that any new kennels would be constructed using a mixture of brick and concrete block with some form of wall insulation. The chart below clearly shows how the construction method improves the level of insulation.

The use of timber in kennels is considered totally unacceptable.
The harsh environment in kennels does not lend itself to the use of timber; it is too easily damaged by chewing and scratching, it is impossible to clean and disinfect once the surface has been damaged, it harbours bacteria and viruses.

CONSTRUCTION	U – value
Brickwork - Solid wall, unplastered 105mm 220mm	3.3 2.3
Brickwork/lightweight concrete block wall (unventilated) with 105mm brick outer leaf and 100mm block inner with 16mm dense plaster face	0.96
As above with 13mm polystyrene board in cavity.	0.70
Solid concrete block wall 190mm with 20mm render on outer face.	2.44

Floors

It is generally accepted that any form of floor within a modern kennel building has to be of a solid nature, i.e. concrete, with a finishing surface over the top, see chapter on floor finishes.

Roofs

The table below shows different U - values for pitched roofs.

CONSTRUCTION METHOD	U – value
Tiles on battens, roofing felt and rafters, 10mm foil backed plasterboard	1.5
Profiled cement sheeting	6.1
As above but with 50mm glass - fibre between joists	0.50
As above but with 25mm glass - fibre insulation between sheets	1.1
Corrugated plastic coated steel sheeting.	6.7
As above with cavity and aluminium foil - backed, 10mm plasterboard.	2.0

INSULATING MATERIALS

<u>The most common materials used to provide insulation for walls, ceilings & floors are:</u>

MATERIAL	THERMAL CONDUCTIVITY and DENSITY
Glass fibre	0.04 W/m° C 12 kg/m^3
Perlight	0.05 W/m° C 175 kg/m^3
Polyurethane	0.032 W/m° C 30 kg/m^3
Polystyrene	0.037 W/m° C 15 kg/m^3
Cellular glass	0.04 W/m° C 135 kg/m^3
Mineral fibre	0.04 W/m° C 16 kg/m^3

It is easy to see how polystyrene and polyurethane are highly effective insulators; this combined with their low weight make them highly suitable for roof insulation particularly in domestic situations or where neighbours are not in close proximity to the kennels. However, in locations where noise could be a problem it might be worth considering the installation of one of the heavy insulators such as perlight. These dense, heavy materials will help reduce the amount of noise breakout from the kennels through the roof.

Cautionary Note
Vermin, most rodents will attack polyurethane and polystyrene insulation. If you live in a rural location or suffer from rodent damage it will be better to use fibreglass as an insulating material as this does not seem so attractive to rodents

3.3 THE CHARTERED INSTITUTE OF ENVIRONMENTAL HEALTH

In 1993 the CIEH published comprehensive guidance notes in the form of the 'Model Licence Conditions and Guidance for Dog and Cat Boarding Establishments'.

The publication's aim was to provide a framework for all local authority inspectors to ensure that a consistent approach was implemented, nation-wide, for kennel sizes, systems for hygiene control and standards.

The local authority has a duty to inspect annually and issue a licence for all boarding kennels and catteries. The inspectors normally come from the Environmental Health Department, this being the obvious choice as they are used to inspecting food outlets, restaurants, etc.

It is worth remembering that the guidance notes suggest the minimum standards and are open to a great deal of latitude. It has been accepted that it is impossible to bring all of the boarding establishments up to the required standard overnight, this will need to be phased in over a period of time for existing kennels.

In new establishments there is an expectation that all of the conditions will be met before a licence is granted.

Cautionary Note
(Where an existing establishment has a licence and the property is sold, it should be borne in mind that the new owner might be required to upgrade the kennels at the outset. Clearly, this will have serious financial implications and will require careful research.)

The CIEH do not have any jurisdiction over animal welfare centres and charities, as they are not commercial boarding establishments. However, from experience, it is the animal welfare centres and charities that are setting the trends and standards for kennels with new designs and environment enriching measures.

3.4   KENNEL SIZES & DESIGNS

The design and layout of the main kennel unit can be as simple or as grand as you want it to be. The size and design will be influenced by financial restrictions, the size of the site, proximity of neighbours, the number of kennels you need to build and any existing buildings that may be used.

In general, all kennel buildings serve to provide the same aim - "a warm, dry environment in which to house dogs". However, all designs are very subjective and can be improved and enriched with minor changes. Before employing a surveyor/architect to produce plans of the proposed site it is worth thinking about the current legislation in terms of kennel and exercise run size and requirements.

It is surprising how even very basic sketches can help to develop a workable plan. Remember, the architect is being employed by you – if you are happy to let him/her take over the entire project without any of your imput, then don't be too upset if the proposal does not match your ideals! *Remember - you have the animal knowledge.*

The CIEH insist that all new kennels must have an exercise run attached to the sleeping quarters, with a sliding hatch to separate the two compartments, the sizes given are: -

- **Sleeping area – minimum of 1.9m^2**
- **Exercise run – minimum of 2.46m^2**

Although these sizes are adequate for animals in boarding kennels, which by their nature only tend to hold animals for a short duration, the average being 1-3 weeks, they are totally inadequate for the more specialist operations such as welfare centres and quarantine kennels. Careful consideration should be given to the nature of the dogs in your care; the facilities for these centres need to take into account all of these additional requirements.

The minimum standard sizes I would recommend are:

Sleeping area -	1500mm deep x 2000mm long (3m^2)
	1500mm deep x 2400mm long (3.6m^2)
Exercise area -	2000mm wide x 2500mm long (5m^2)
	2400mm wide x 2500mm long (6m^2)
Circulation corridors -	1200mm - 1500mm wide

Clearly, all of the above kennels and exercise runs are far larger than the minimum.

However, I feel that these sizes give a good compromise in terms of the animals' needs, cost and staff time for cleaning, etc. This, combined with the fact that the animals in the care of charities and good boarding kennels receive lots of human interaction e.g. grooming, exercise away from the kennels, all helps to combat the effects of stress and to make for a much happier and more relaxed dog.

As I have already stated, by its very nature a kennel building has to be robust and designed for a hard life. However this does not mean that it has to be austere and prison like. Kennel design has improved tremendously over the past two or three years and continues to be an exciting area for development.

Due to environmental pressures, local authorities and welfare centres have started looking at kennel design, particularly in relation to noise. Although initially this was in relation to the Environmental Protection Act 1990, it has given impetus to all involved with dogs to look at and try to establish which designs provide a better environment.

The style and design of the kennel is very subjective and all of the designs mentioned below all have their advantages and disadvantages. The preferred style is a matter of personal choice and is influenced by several factors.

Below are some of the more common designs that are in use. These are:

- Double banked barrack block.
- Single banked barrack block.
- Circular (Parasol).
- H style.
- L shaped.
- Square with separate wings.

DOUBLE BANK - STRAIGHT LINE BARRACK BLOCK

This has been the traditional style for many years, and even today still proves to be a design that has many benefits.
It is a versatile design that will suit a large variety of sites.

Advantages
- Modular style that can be extended to suit the individual's needs.
- Cost effective.
- Can be sub - divided into smaller units. This is an important feature particularly for boarding kennels, this flexible design means that sections, if not in use, can have the heating/lighting turned off.
- Simple construction.

Disadvantages
- Due to the linear configuration, it can generate extremely high levels of noise, particularly if you have to walk through one section to get to another.
- Larger units will involve having to walk the full length of the corridor in order to reach the end kennels, again resulting in high levels of disturbance to the dogs.
- Little privacy for nervous/quiet animals.
- Only one aspect will face South/South West.

SINGLE BANKED

This has been a favourite design for many years. It is generally considered more relaxing to work in than a large, double-banked style.

Advantages
- Modular style, can be extended or reduced to suit.
- Suitable for a wide variety of sites.
- Less 'wind-up' factor to the dogs, they do not have a kennel facing them; this obviously results in less noise.
- The building can be orientated to face South/South West.

Disadvantages
- More expensive pro-rata than the double banked unit.
- Limited practical length of building, a building with twenty kennels will be in excess of 30 metres in length.
- Can feel very claustrophobic with narrow corridors and limited natural light.

CIRCULAR

This unique and radical design was first used at the Wood Green Animal Shelter in Cambridgeshire over twelve years ago. Since its conception the design has been modified and improved.

Today it is widely used by the National Canine Defence League (NCDL) and the Scottish Society for the Prevention of Cruelty to Animals (SSPCA).

The design is based on a twelve-metre diameter circle with a central core. This is divided into twelve equal segments, giving eleven kennels and an entrance lobby and combined kitchen.

Each kennel has direct access to its exercise run via a sliding hatch.

The rationale behind the design was to create a striking, practical, functional unit with sound reducing qualities.

Advantages
- Complies with current CIEH standards.
- Simplified heating and ventilation systems.
- Ease of staff use.
- Public viewing can be limited to the outer exercise runs leaving the inner core as a sanctuary for the dogs.
- Unusual styling.

Disadvantages
- Styling, this will not suit all locations and local authorities, although some approve of the design favouring it over traditional systems.
- The standard design entails the staff going outside the building to gain access into the exercise runs.
- Limited space for ancillary rooms.
- The site needs to be securely fenced due to the lack of a safety corridor.
- High cost per kennel.
- Large number of dogs facing each other; this can increase the noise levels and stress.
- The floor can prove difficult to ensure the correct slope and falls.

H SHAPED, L SHAPED & SQUARE WITH WINGS

These three designs all have the potential to provide highly suitable accommodation for the modern kennel. In general, what makes these styles suitable is their flexibility and generally smaller numbers of dogs per kennel block than previously used.

All of these designs are suitable for either single banked or double-banked configurations.

Advantages
- Modular construction, additional wings can be added.
- The wings can be of unequal length to suit the location.
- Non-animal related operations can be carried out without going into the main kennels.
- Can be either single or double banked.
- Allows for soft landscaping in front of the buildings to increase the aesthetic qualities and remove the sterile harsh look often associated with kennels.
- Individual wings can be used to house different types of dogs i.e. small, large, old or nervous. This reduces the number of visitors that may need to view the dogs, as sections can be dedicated for the various types/categories of dog.
- Reduced risk of infection.
- Reduction in noise levels.
- Wings can be closed down for maintenance or infection problems.

Disadvantages
- Generally smaller buildings will be more expensive per kennel than larger units.
- Careful consideration should be given to the final proposed design and layout.
- Could prove more difficult to construct a larger number of kennels on a smaller site.

FIGURES 7 – 12 SHOW VARIOUS DESIGNS

Barrack Block Kennels

Drawings courtesy of
FORUM ARCHITECTS

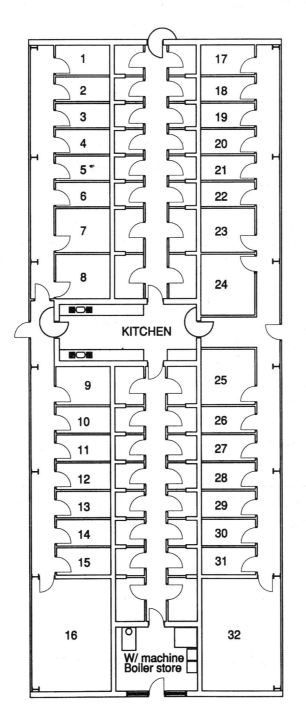

Barrack Block (double)

Drawings courtesy of
FORUM ARCHITECTS

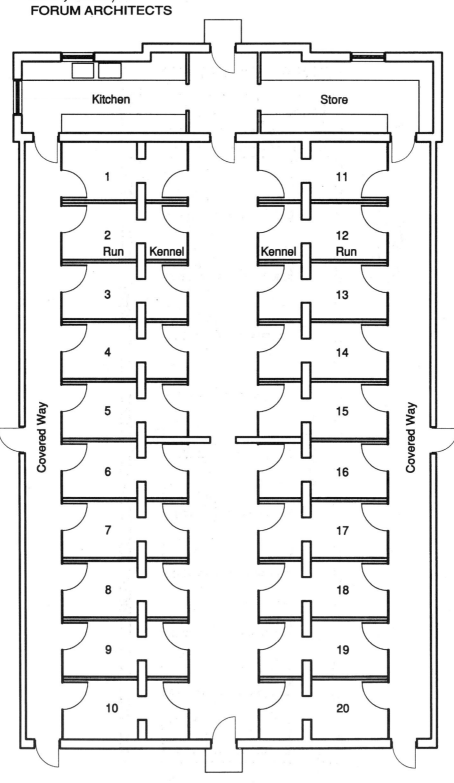

Barrack Block (single)

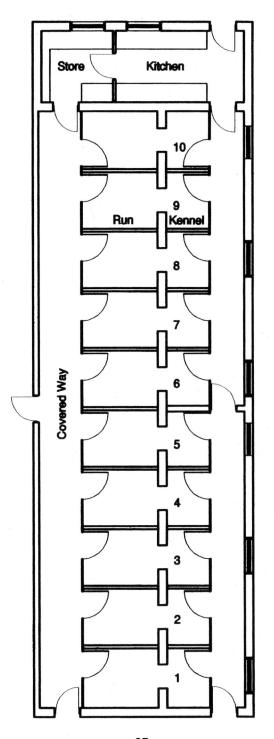

Drawings courtesy of
FORUM ARCHITECTS

Typical Parasol Kennel

Drawings courtesy of
FORUM ARCHITECTS

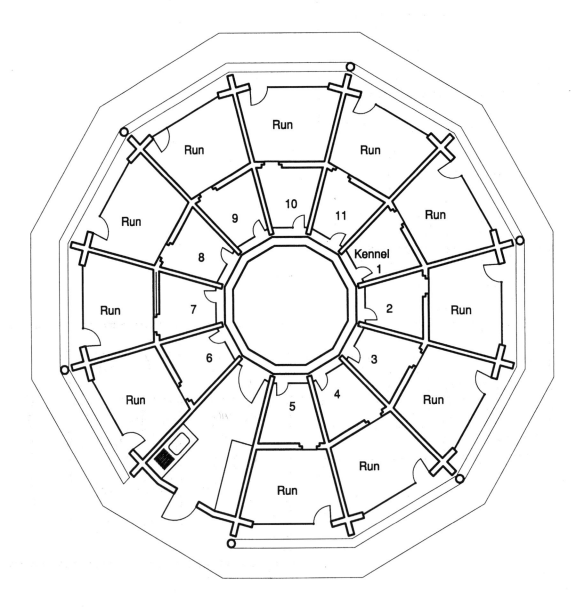

Proposed new style Kennel

Drawings courtesy of
FORUM ARCHITECTS

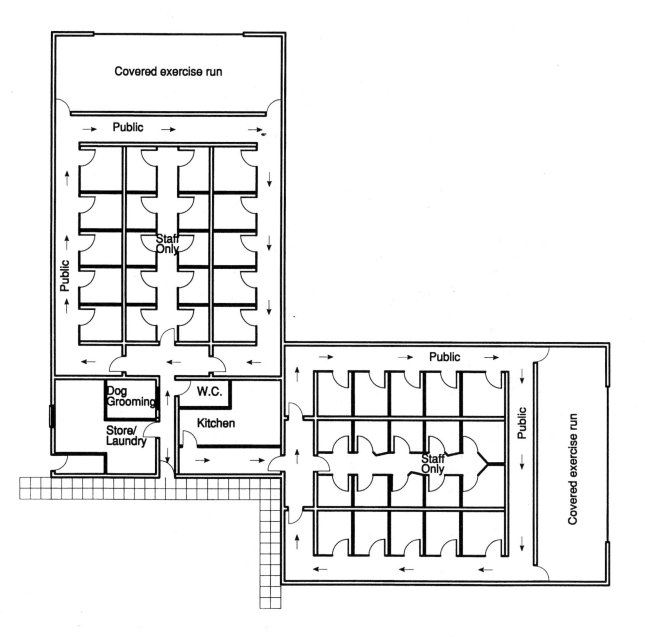

Suggested Internal Kennel Design Showing Offset Panels

Drawings courtesy of
FORUM ARCHITECTS

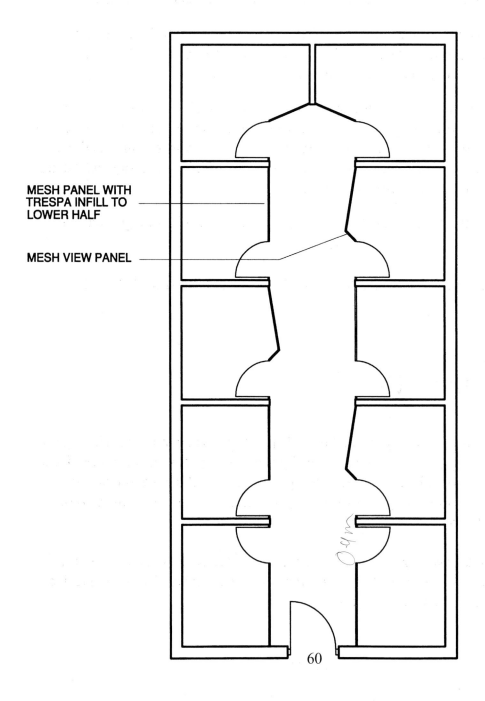

MESH PANEL WITH
TRESPA INFILL TO
LOWER HALF

MESH VIEW PANEL

3.5   LARGE OPEN EXERCISE RUNS

Although some people frown upon the idea of having large, possibly communal exercise runs in which to allow dogs to run free, I am a firm believer that this facility is highly beneficial.

It not only provides the option to allow off-lead exercise, it also allows the dog to get away from the main kennel building for a short period of time. This factor alone can make a remarkable difference to how the dog reacts to the kennel environment.

Clearly the cost of providing such a facility can be expensive; 1800mm-2200mm chainlink fencing is approximately £35.00 per linear metre. Fencing of this height will prevent all but the most agile of dogs from escaping.

The obvious weak point for any type of fencing is at ground level. However, for most boarding, breeding and welfare kennels providing fencing that is securely pegged down at 1 metre intervals will be sufficient to prevent dogs from escaping under it. This of course assumes that the fence runs level with the ground and any undulations are infilled with soil and seeded with grass.

Obviously for quarantine kennels the wire will need to be set into the ground and concreted.

Fencing is one problem, another is the type of surface you provide. The main options are:

1. Grass.
2. Concrete.
3. Block paving/paving slabs.
4. Tarmac.

1. **Grass** - This is the cheapest solution and apart from regular mowing will require little maintenance. It works exceptionally well for locations that do not receive a large amount of animal traffic and have good drainage. It looks aesthetically pleasing and is generally considered a surface that is 'dog friendly' in terms of reducing the possibility of injury.

    The main disadvantages are that it cannot be disinfected, is weather dependent and will quickly become churned up around entrances/exits. This might preclude its use during the winter months.

2   **Concrete** - The three prime considerations with concrete are cost, aesthetics and time/labour to keep it clean. A large expanse of concrete does not look aesthetically pleasing, it is costly to install, approximately £20 to £25m^2 and will require staff time to maintain it in a clean condition.

The advantage with this finish is that it is suitable for all year-round use. Careful consideration should be given to the finish; too coarse and it will be uncomfortable for the dogs to walk on and difficult to sweep/clean.
Too polished a surface and it will be extremely slippery for dogs and staff, particularly when wet.

The other point to consider is drainage; most local authorities will deem that a hard-surfaced exercise run should have the same drainage provision as the main kennels, i.e. it should be connected to the foul drainage system. If so, you should look closely at the demands that could be placed upon your drainage system when it rains!

3   **Block paving/paving slabs** - Both of these options offer a most aesthetically pleasing surface. They come in a wide range of finishes, colours, textures and sizes, are able to withstand daily cleaning and do not readily discolour with the use of disinfectants or urine. Of the two options, my preference is for paving slabs; due to their larger size it reduces the amount of joints required.

4   **Tarmac -** This is an alternative material I have seen used. Although initially it appears to be a suitable surface, it has many disadvantages. The surface is extremely porous and will allow water/urine to soak through to the base layer and it can get extremely hot during the summer, making it uncomfortable/dangerous for the dogs to lie on.

The other main disadvantage with it is that when the sun warms it, it softens; this can lead to problems with the stones/tarmac sticking to the dogs' feet. I have also seen it where a dog has dug up large sections in very little time.

3.6   FLOOR FINISHES

As I have already stated, any form of finish used in kennels has to start with a concrete/screed base; timber floors, even with a covering over the top, are not suitable. The top wearing finish has to be water/urine/faeces/disinfectant resistant, durable, quick drying, long lasting and tough enough to withstand the damage caused by the dogs.

The resin flooring industry is complex and serves a wide range of markets; each market having its own individual requirement for chemical resistance, cleanability, etc. The similarity of the products causes confusion and this makes it difficult to obtain like-for-like quotations. I believe the number of suitable finishes is limited.

However, within the categories, the choice is limitless and this is where the difficulties and problems start to arise.

<u>The common systems used in kennels are:</u>

1. Floor paints, sealers.
2. High build coatings.
3. Self smooth screed.
4. Resin screeds.
5. Terrazzo.
6. Polymer screeds.
7. Granolithic screeds.
8. Vinyl sheet.
9. Floor tiles.

FLOOR CLASSIFICATION
Paint, sealer: (50-250 microns thick) Finish is applied with a brush/roller.
High build coating: 0.4-1.0mm (400-1000 microns thick). Normally applied with a roller.
Flow applied coatings: 2mm-3mm thick. This is poured onto the floor and spread around with a trowel to form an uniformed thickness.
Screed: 4mm-12mm thick depending on the type. This is applied with a steel trowel.
Tiles: 8mm-10mm thick, self finish

Floor Slope

The normal and preferred way to lay a floor within a kennel is to cast a level concrete slab, then lay a sand/cement screed over the top. It is this screed that is laid to falls, i.e. a slope falling from the rear of the kennel to the drainage channel at the front of the kennel, the screed is then covered by the final finishing material.

For the kennel to be self-draining i.e. the water runs naturally into the drainage channel without too much mopping, etc the fall has to be a minimum of 1:80, a fall of 1:60 will give a much better results.

This means that if you have a kennel that is 1500mm deep from front to back, it will require a screed of 50mm at the front and 75mm at the rear to achieve a fall of 1:60.

Obviously, the fall can be increased to create a more pronounced slope to provide better water run-off, however, this has to be set against the increased material and labour costs involved. Even with a fall of 1:60 some water will remain and may need to be mopped up.

The final choice of wearing course is normally decided by finances, the amount of use the kennels will receive and the type of dog being kennelled. For example if you operate boarding kennels which are only used for a small part of the year, do you really want to specify a finish which will last for fifty years of hard daily use?

By approaching this decision with a flexible attitude you should be able to specify the correct product for your requirements.

Undoubtedly a cheaper product cannot be expected to last indefinitely, but as long as this has been taken into consideration and resources/time are made available to carry out any remedial works, this should not be a problem.

However, in the case of a large animal welfare charity that operates at full capacity throughout the year, it is extremely difficult and time consuming to have to empty and close down a kennel building in order to carry out maintenance works.
The correct choice of suitable materials for your situation is probably one of the most important decisions you will have to make.

An incorrect choice can make life extremely difficult and expensive in the long-term, with unplanned remedial works, floors that are unhygienic, resulting in bad odours and damp conditions, etc.

I would strongly recommend that if you decide that an expensive finish is required and you cannot afford the first or most suitable option, that you adopt a flexible approach.

This can take the form of:

- A reduction in the number of kennels originally proposed
- An omission of some ancillary rooms
- A section of the kennels having the proposed finish with the remainder having a cheap paint finish in order to bring the kennels on-line. Accepting the fact that this is only a short-term measure and will require the correct finish when finances allow.

1.   Floor paints and sealers (50-250 microns)

These systems are the minimum required to satisfy the CIEH and provide a non-porous, washable and hygienic surface. They range from single pack waterbased to two-part solvent based epoxy and polyurethane systems, they are all basically paint thickness coverings.

As they are classified as paints/sealers they are relatively thin and therefore cannot be expected to last more than one/two years before requiring to be redecorated. The application of additional coats is a simple, straightforward task; the old finish needs to be dry, clean and well prepared in readiness for the new coating.

To achieve a suitable 'key' it may require the use of a floor sanding machine or the use of acids. It is a waste of time simply to wash down the kennels and over-coat with the new finish; it will flake off in no time at all! For a charity this type of finish is totally inadequate for the kennel environment and is limited to store rooms, etc.

2.   High build coatings (400-1000 microns)

Like floor paints, coatings come in a range of guises and colours, on the whole they are two-part systems and require specialist installation. Obviously, the thicker coatings of approximately 1000 microns will be more resistant than a thinner one.

However, at present, I have to say that I am still extremely wary about using this type of product in the main kennel building. Once again its use is limited to ancillary areas.

3. Flow applied coating (2.0-3.0mm)

Flow applied coatings or self-smoothing are two part systems and are, I believe, the minimum required for use in the kennel environment which will provide a surface with a reasonable life span.

Although still relatively thin they should last for approximately four/six years before remedial work is required.

The inclusion of a fine aggregate into the finished surface is something to consider; it will _help_ prevent dogs/staff slipping. The coarseness of the aggregate is a personal decision, my general guideline is to try and achieve a finish similar to that of orange peel. Too coarse and it will hold the dirt and be difficult to clean, too fine and it will be of little benefit.

4. Epoxy/Polyurethane screeds (4.0mm-6.0mm)

It is normal for an epoxy/polyurethane screed to be laid to an average thickness of 4-6mm; this is applied by the use of a steel trowel. Obviously, the cost for this type of screed starts to become noticeably more expensive than compared to a coating. The time factor alone is considerably greater, particularly when installing into small, individual kennels which have been laid to falls (an approximate cost to install this type of product into an area of around 100m sq. will be in the region of £35 to £50).

Again, an aggregate should be included, in addition to this it is common practice to incorporate a surface-sealing coat to reduce porosity. This surface coat will help prevent staining and spoiling of the screed.

Correctly installed, an epoxy/polyurethane screed will look extremely aesthetic, provide a durable, hygienic finish and last for many years without requiring any remedial works.

Advantages

- Gives a seamless and hygienic finish.
- Semi-gloss finish.
- Full range of attractive colours.
- Cost effective.
- Slip resistance. The inclusion of fine aggregates between coats will give varying degree of slip resistance depending on the size of the aggregate.
- Fast installation.
- Non-professional installation for coatings/sealers.

Disadvantages

- The quality of the system and finish is highly dependent upon the quality of the contractor. In addition, the finish may also vary throughout the building even using the same contractor and product.
- A high degree of preparation is required to ensure a suitable 'key' to existing coatings.
- Limited durability - (this is extremely subjective and is influenced by external factors such as correct preparation, product choice, cleaning regimes, use, etc.)
- Possible reaction with existing coatings. (It is important to write down the manufacturer/product specification of any existing coatings used to ensure future compatibility).
- Any unevenness in the substrate will be reflected in the coating.
- Coatings can be damaged/removed by use of a hot or cold pressure washer.
- Discoloration can be a major problem, i.e. disinfectants and urine.

Summary of Applied Resin Based Systems.

These systems have many good features; they have been used extensively in factories, hospitals and breweries for many years and still continue to be used. I believe that they have failed in kennel environments primarily because of incorrect specification. Certainly, from my point of view, being the person responsible for specifying and procuring the work.

I don't believe that most people understand how harsh a kennel environment can be.

If you choose an applied finish, whether it is a simple paint or an expensive screed, these are some of the points you should consider:

- Use a reputable company and ensure that they make a site visit to familiarise themselves with the particular project and any problems that might occur, i.e. epoxy screeds do not allow for any movement, while polyurethane screeds have a small amount of flexibility. This is an important point particularly when dealing with buildings, which have shown signs of movement.

- Explain fully what the product is to be used for and how much use it will receive. Obtain a written guarantee from the manufacturers stating that the recommended product will achieve the required standard.

- For you to appreciate future remedial works that will be required, obtain a time frame/guidance from the suppliers, again this is extremely subjective and will be influenced by external factors.

- Check with the company that your chosen cleaning products will not damage the finish. I have seen some epoxy screeds discoloured by the use of disinfectants; although the product was not damaged, it left unsightly indelible staining.

- Compatibility – ensure that any new coating will not react with any previously applied, keep all data sheets.

- Pressure washer - If you use a hot power washer to clean the kennels check on the maximum heat that can be used on the coating/screed before it will affect the surface; it can be quite low.

- Ask for working references of the material you propose to use, a visual inspection of the product being used under normal everyday working conditions is highly recommended.

Cautionary Note

Check to see if your building has a damp-proof membrane (DPM) most older agricultural buildings don't. Without one, this could cause a failure of the finish. If in doubt ask a local builder to carry out some investigative work to establish one way or the other.

It is also worth checking the small print of the contract to see what clauses apply to a possible failure of the floor due to movement/dampness.

Again, all of these issues can be addressed by using a reputable company.

5.   Terrazzo

This is a natural product based on cement and decorative aggregates, usually marble. It comes in the form of tiles or can be laid in situ.

It was used extensively in veterinary/human hospitals, particularly during the 60's and 70's and considered, at that time, to be the most suitable floor system available.

Advantages
- Virtually indestructible.
- Range of colours.

Disadvantages
- High initial cost.
- Noisy.
- Hard on impact.
- Extremely slippery when wet - any form of soap, water or disinfectant can result in an extremely dangerous slippery surface.
- Discoloration - Can be prone to discoloration from disinfectants containing cresols or phenols.
- High level of skill required to produce a satisfactory finish.

Summary - Although terrazzo is extremely durable and aesthetically pleasing, I believe that the disadvantages outweigh the advantages.

My particular concerns relate to the dangers of slipping to both staff and animals. It has its place in entrance lobbies of hotels and shopping centres but it has been superseded for kennel applications.

6.   Polymer screeds

Polymer screeds are based on cement and selected aggregates with liquid styrene butadience copolymere being added to the mix. They are better known for their applications for industrial situations, particularly in wet areas such as breweries and fish processing.

Although still popular for industry they are not particularly well known for kennel applications.

Advantages
- Can be laid as a thin screed, i.e. 10-12mm thick is sufficient for most applications.
- Simple installation.
- Jointless, in small areas.
- Anti-slip aggregates can be incorporated.
- Resistant to oils and acids.
- Suitable for wet environments.
- Suitable for steam cleaning.
- Range of colours.
- Cost effective.

Disadvantages
- The quality of the finish is dependent upon the operative to ensure a uniform finish

Summary - Although not widely used for kennel applications, it can be used to overcome problem or damaged areas.

I have seen it used to overlay some damaged and rough concrete exercise runs and it has proved to be extremely durable, easy to clean and has not discoloured or stained.

From my limited experience with this product I would quite readily use it again.

7.   Granolithic

This is a natural material based on cement and selected aggregates; it is normally laid with a minimum thickness of 50mm.

This is a durable and long lasting surface, however with time some dusting may occur. To prevent this and increase its durability an application of sodium silicate hardener is normally applied. Sprinkling the surface whilst still wet, with carborundum powder will add a degree of slip resistance.

Its main use today is in commercial and industrial applications.

Advantages -
- Extremely durable and does not damage easily.

Disadvantages -
- High initial cost.
- Aesthetics - As this is a cement based product it has the same dull grey/brown colour as concrete.
- Quality - In order to provide a satisfactory finish a high level of skill and supervision is required. It also requires careful attention to detail in order to prevent cracking and crazing at a later date.
- Porous - Will need some form of sealing agent.

Summary - Although it is used in industry it has little to offer the kennel owner. Its poor aesthetic qualities and specialist application has meant that alternative products have superseded it.

8.   Vinyl sheet

Although not recommended for use in main kennel units, these finishes are highly suitable for ancillary rooms, such as receptions and laundries.

The commercial quality sheets available have been used extensively in canteens, kitchens and hospitals for many years. They are available in different grades, patterns and with varying degrees of slip resistance, this being achieved by the use of profiles or with silicon carbide and aluminium oxide particles incorporated within the finish.

Advantages
- Range of colours and textures.
- Can be coved up the wall for improved hygiene.
- Joints can be heat welded to form a continuous, hygienic and watertight finish.
- Warm and quiet - Although not generally suitable in the main kennels, it is used in veterinary hospitals for recovery kennels, for both floors and walls, with good results.

Disadvantages
- Can be damaged by sharp objects.
- It melts on contact with cigarettes.

Summary - Vinyl sheeting has many applications for the kennel owner, it is aesthetically pleasing and extremely versatile.

For a welfare centre it is limited to ancillary rooms.

However, for hospitals or owners of non-destructive dogs it can be used in the main kennel units to good effect.

9.   Tiles

When talking about tiles we are only concerned with unglazed, vitrified tiles with low water absorption qualities to class BI.

All ceramic tiles are manufactured from natural, i.e. clay, felspar and quartz; and have been used extensively in industrial, commercial and healthcare applications for many years.

During the 1980's there was a trend to use alternative, seamless finishes to improve the hygienic qualities, hence the increase in resin based systems. However with suitable grouting and disinfectants any concerns relating to their use in kennels are totally unfounded.

The standard sizes used are 150mm x 150mm or 300mm x 300mm.

Slip resistance - Some floors have higher risks of slipping than others. There is a number of contributing factors:

- Type of material used.
- Presence of water, fats or disinfectants.
- Physical handling of dogs in confined spaces.
- Type of footwear used.

All of these matters will influence the slip resistance of a floor. At present only Germany has set standards of slip resistance for floors in commercial, industrial and barefoot areas. It is likely that this will become the standard used by all European Community countries in the near future.

The system used by the German government to assess and measure the level of slip resistance is known as the " R-value" for commercial, industrial uses and A, B, or C value for barefoot areas. The higher this value, the more slip resistance the tile has.

The capacity to displace water and dirt is measured and known as the "V-value" the higher the V number the greater the space between the studs, the values are V4, V6, V8 and V10.

Obviously the greater the space between the studs and the deeper the profile, the greater is the amount of water that can be dealt with before the floor becomes dangerous.

SLIP RESISTNACE IN COMMERCIAL APPLICATIONS	
SLIP ANGLE°	**R - VALUE**
From 3° to 10°	R - 9
From 10° to 19°	R - 10
From 19° to 27°	R - 11
From 27° to 35°	R - 12
More than 35°	R - 13

BAREFOOT AREAS	
SLIP ANGLE°	**V - VALUE**
Minimum slip angle - 12°	A
Minimum slip angle - 18°	B
Minimum slip angle - 24°	C

Advantages
- Uniform finish.
- Durable and virtually maintenance free *(having been in use in kennels for over fifteen years of constant daily use, they still look pristine and remain hygienic. I do not foresee that we will have to carry out any remedial works).*
- Range of colours and slip resistance.
- Resistance to most acids and alkalis *(all of the units we have tiles in have not suffered in terms of discoloration or staining; this cannot be said about epoxy based systems).*
- Highly suitable for hot water power washing.
- They are not affected by solar radiation, which means they are fade resistant.
- Simple installation, providing the correct fall has been incorporated to the screed floor.

Disadvantages
- High initial cost - particularly with an epoxy grout.
- High R and V values can be difficult to clean.

Summary - Due to the heavy use charity kennels receive on a daily basis, I would recommend vitrified tiles as being the most suitable as a long-term solution to the flooring problem. They stand the test of time, once cleaned they look like new.

Typical specification used by a large welfare organisation

On opening a technical catalogue it can seem a little daunting at first, with all of the R and V values for industrial and barefoot areas. Obviously for kennel applications some careful thought is required; to force a dog to sleep and use a kennel with a floor tile with high values would be cruel and highly uncomfortable and would result in soreness and foot problems.

Therefore a suitable compromise has to be made:

CORRIDORS - Clearly, this is the highest risk area for staff and animals, due to the fact that an element of speed can be introduced.
TILE - R-10 or R-11 with a V6 rating.

KENNEL SLEEPING AREAS - As stated a compromise has to be made for the comfort of the animal, due to the fact that the sleeping area is a relatively small area this reduces the opportunity for brisk movement or being pulled around by a large dog.
TILE - R-9 smooth.

New Developments - Some of the major manufacturers have recently brought out riven patterned vitrified tiles. These are proving to be an excellent compromise for the kennel environment.

They have sufficient texture to prevent slipping for staff and animals but are easy to clean and mop over. Therefore they are highly suitable for use in the sleeping areas and corridors.

Covings

The CIEH insist that all new kennels have a radiused coving between the vertical and horizontal sections.

<u>This is normally achieved in one of four ways, either:</u>

1. **Tiles** - All manufacturers have floor systems that allow for the use of a sit - on, traditional flush fitting or flushfit coved skirtings with internal and external angles. Providing the layout has been designed to accommodate these finishing pieces, they work extremely effectively. The finishing pieces can be expensive and care should be taken to ensure that they have been included with the main floor and not looked upon as an extra.

   Helpful Hints -

   📖 Ensure that the flooring contractor allows for the necessary expansion joints between the vertical/horizontal and also in front of floor drainage channels
   📖 The flushfit skirting provides the easiest coving to clean; it has a more radiused corner.

2. **Epoxy** - This system is extremely effective; it is basically a mixture of fine aggregates and epoxy resin, which is formed into a smooth coved skirting, normally 50mm high. The finish can self colour or be over-coated with a coloured finish. It is a quick and relatively cheap system, suitable for adding at a later date during remedial works in order to bring the kennels up to a better standard, it is extremely durable, jointless and gives a professional finish.

3. **Granolithic -** This system will provide an excellent coving, which complies with the CIEH rules. However it is generally more expensive to install than epoxy and is not as durable. The level of skill required to ensure a smooth, hygienic finish is far greater than that for epoxy and there is a tendency for it to develop fine hairline cracks.

4. **Sand/Cement -** Sand/cement can be used in a similar fashion to that of epoxy. It is easy to install, cost effective and can be overpainted to give a more professional appearance. If you opt for this system ensure that you use fine-grained sand and add PVA to the mixture to ensure a smooth finish that is strong and waterproof.

3.7 WALL FINISHES

Like floor coverings, the range of products suitable for walls is virtually endless. The primary aim of overcoating concrete block walls is to improve the hygienic qualities of the building, i.e. to prevent dirt, faeces, urine, and bacteria/viruses being ingrained in the open, porous nature of block.

The second benefit is to improve the aesthetic qualities of the building; most concrete blocks tend to be dull grey or brown colours, with suitable finishes these can be dramatically improved.

The more common finishes used are:

1. Masonry paint.
2. Single or twin pack epoxy or polyurethane systems.
3. Rubber based paint.
4. Dense render.
5. Tiles.
6. Cladding materials, i.e. Trespa Metion or plastic boarding.
7. Engineering bricks with waterproof mortar.

Helpful Hints -

☐ If you are planning to apply a paint finish, whatever type, to concrete blockwork, ensure that you specify a high, quality paint grade block. A coarse open textured block is not suitable for a paint finish; even with three or four coats, the open texture will be difficult to seal and will not give a long lasting, pleasing appearance.

☐ If you intend to apply ceramic tiles, then the cheapest block will be sufficient.

1. Masonry paint

This is probably the cheapest system on the market that is suitable for both interior and exterior uses in the kennel environment. Most are water or acrylic based, easy to apply and can be applied during most conditions.

The large range of colours and types available enable you to choose a suitable product for either new or refurbishment work. If you opt for this system for interior use, ensure that you specify a smooth, sheen finish; this will make it far easier to clean.

In most kennels it is the lower 1200mm of blockwork that is subjected to most wear and tear; above this height there tends to be little damage. Because of the relatively low cost and ease of application it is a system that needs to be redecorated every three or four years is required.

2. Single and twin pack epoxy/polyurethane paints

Like the floor coatings, the number of systems available in this category is immense, with a large number of companies all selling what appear to be the same product, and this is where the problems start. It is a question of correctly specifying a suitable product that will withstand the harsh environment in kennels.

Most of these systems require a higher level of application with better preparation and cleaning than for masonry paints. Correctly specified, they provide a tough, hard wearing, chemically resistant finish. This category of finish has probably the greatest choice of colours.

3. Acrylated rubber

This product has been used extensively for industrial and commercial applications for many years. It is a single pack system, for non-skilled application and is normally brush applied; it is highly suitable for damp environments and areas subject to frequent washing down.

The range of colours is slightly limited, although it is sufficient for most situations. Unlike epoxy or polyurethane finishes the surface is softer and can be scratched by persistent animals, although I have not found this to be of any major concern and any minor damage can be easily repaired.

Summary of Applied Wall Finishes.

You should ensure that whatever system you choose is suitable for your requirements. I would strongly advise against using a new product from an unknown company. Remember that when the time comes for redecorating you need to be able to purchase the same product as you originally used.

Most of the professional paints are based on a system of application, i.e. matching primers and undercoats with two or three top coats; they have been designed as a system and are therefore not suitable for mixing and matching. This is something I cannot over emphasise; whatever system used, remember to keep the data sheets or a record of the product.

The other point to consider is the use of hot power washers; most of these paints will not tolerate high temperatures, i.e. over 80°C. This is not normally a problem providing the operator is aware of this and sprays a fine mist, rather than trying to clean the walls by concentrating one particular spot.

4. Dense render

Although this is not a common finish for kennel interiors I have seen it used. Correctly applied this finish will give a durable, smooth, easy to clean and hygienic finish, the drawback with this finish is its drab grey colour. It does not give the impression of a modern, well-designed kennel building.

The only way to compensate for this is to apply either a paint finish or tiles over it; clearly this makes it an extremely expensive finish. It is far better to specify the correct materials in the first place.

The other disadvantage of this system, apart from the aesthetic qualities is the cost. It requires a high level of skill and supervision to produce an even, uniform finish throughout the building. Another problem associated with these strong mixes is their tendency to shrinkage, cracking and movement.

5. Tiles

Unlike floor tiles, which are designed to withstand far higher forces and damage, wall tiles are quite fragile. Most people are aware of the standard type of wall tiles available in the DIY stores; tiles used in kennels are no different. The most popular sizes used are 150mm x 150mm, 200mm x 100mm or 200mm x 200mm, and can have a gloss or matt finishes. I would always specify a gloss finish due to its ease of cleaning.

Clearly, the cost of installing tiles even if only for the first 1200mm high, this being the main area that receives the most wear and tear is still extremely high. However, once installed they will last for many years without requiring any remedial works. It is a matter of deciding what level of time and money you have or want to spend on future maintenance.

6. Cladding finishes

There are some excellent materials available for cladding, e.g. Trespa Metion or Perstorp Wareite. Both products come in a large range of colours, grades, weights and are extremely durable, can withstand most chemicals and scratching from dogs. The drawback with these products is their cost; an 8mm-thick board will cost in the region of £38.00m^2.

In order to prevent ingress of water and urine, etc. the board requires to be professionally fixed and sealed. Although they are highly suitable for many uses in the kennel environment, I would not recommend them for kennel wall cladding on a large scale; there are plenty of more suitable, more cost-effective alternative finishes available.

7. Engineering bricks

This is an alternative to applied finishes. This system gives a durable finish that does not require any future maintenance. Obviously, if you opt for this system this needs to be identified at the outset of the contract. Generally, engineering bricks are used to construct division walls and the lower part of the main building to a height of around 1200mm, this being the area that receives most wear and tear.

The choice of colours in engineering bricks is limited, i.e. beige, red or blue tend to be the standard colours. This might seem rather drab but with suitable floor and wall finishes above the engineering brick it can work extremely well. In order to prevent staining of the mortar, a waterproofing agent will need to be added during the construction stage; an alternative is to paint the joints with a clear epoxy sealer.

Cautionary Note.

If you choose this system, be aware particularly when constructing kennel divisions and using only one brick thickness, i.e. 112mm, that only one face will be true and smooth.

Bricks are not totally square and symmetrical, each will have small variations this is evened out by the mortar joint, the other face will be slightly more irregular.
This leaves you with two options, you accept this and live with it, or you construct a 225mm thick wall; this will give two even faces.

3.8   KENNEL METALWORK AND ASSOCIATED ITEMS

All caging systems used for commercial kennels and welfare centres should be constructed from metal; the use of timber is not suitable, it is outdated and does not conform to current CIEH standards, for all of the reasons already mentioned.

General specification
The design and specification is really your choice, but as a general guide the recognised standard is for 25mm x 25mm box section with 50mm x 50mm x 10g weldmesh infill. Heavier mesh can be used for large dogs; the thickness is normally increased to 8 gauge (4.064mm).

 An alternative to using weldmesh is vertical bars, this being preferred by some owners on the grounds of strength and aesthetics. Although slightly more expensive than weldmesh, it is exceptionally strong, gives better galvanising results and does not break down.

(I have seen a few kennels that have been damaged due to dogs chewing at the weldmesh, this is not the case with the bar system).

The other advantage of the system is that it reduces the chance of a dog escaping by using the door as a climbing frame, as can happen with a weldmesh infill.

The normal specification is for 8mm-bar set at 50mm centres, although this can be altered to suit individual requirements.

The three recognised metal systems are:

- Plain metal with a paint finish.
- Metal that has been hot dipped galvanised.
- Stainless steel.

Plain metal with paint finish

Clearly this will be the cheapest system in the short term. New metal that has had a coloured paint finish looks bright, clean and gives a professional appearance - the normal paints used are Galvafroid or Hammerite. However, once in use these finishes do not last, particularly on the lower sections, these being the areas that receive the most damage from disinfectants, urine and dogs chewing.

After a short period of time the metal will have heavy rust deposits, be unhygienic, have poor aesthetic qualities and will require remedial works. This is where it becomes expensive in time and labour; once rust has taken hold, it will only be a matter of time before you will need to replace it.

Hot dipped galvanised

Galvanising is a process where all the frames and gates, etc. are dipped into a tank containing hot liquid zinc; this forms a chemical bond with the metal, which ensures a protective, durable coating. This coating, provided it is not broken, will last for many years without showing any signs of deterioration (*I have seen metalwork that has been galvanised, some over twenty years old and still in perfect condition*).

It is generally recognised as being the most cost effective, long-term system available.

Stainless steel

Although this is more expensive than galvanised systems, on average around 10% to 20% more and it is a highly suitable material for kennels. The major difference between stainless steel and galvanised steel is that there is no protective barrier to break down; stainless steel is a metal that is resistant to rusting.

Of all the systems it is the most expensive, is possibly the most hygienic, has the best aesthetic qualities and does not have a coating that can break down. The disadvantage of this product is that it requires cleaning to keeping it looking bright and shining.

Kennel partitions

The CIEH recommend that in all new kennels the divisions between each kennel is of a solid nature to a height of 1200mm. This can be achieved by the use of solid galvanised sheets fixed into 25mm box section framing. Although this provides a secure and maintenance free kennel, I would strongly advise against such a system. The main concern is of noise; with the use of so much steel it is surprising how any noise in the kennels is reverberated around the building.

These high noise levels not only make an unpleasant working environment but also increase the stress levels of the animals being cared for. Clearly, the larger number of kennels you have the more pronounced this problem will be.

If you decide to construct divisions using a framed system I suggest that you look at alternative infill panels such as Trespa Metion, Perstorp Compact or Meshlite, all of these products are highly suitable for kennel partitions. As discussed earlier, all are available in a range of grades and colours, are warm to the touch and do not generate the high noise levels of steel sheeting. A thickness of 6mm will be more than adequate for most situations.

Manufacturers of metal systems such as Croft Engineering are able to offer alternative infill panels to suit most applications.

Helpful Hints –

📖 One of the main problems associated with all metal divisions is the amount of noise generated when a dog jumps up and hits the panel; this is particularly noticeable with longer external run panels. One cheap way to overcome this is to install a layer of 25mm insulation, i.e. polyurethane/polystyrene between the original galvanised sheet then fix another sheet over the insulation.

    If you opt for a framed system to provide the partitions you will have to ensure that each panel is measured individually to take into account the variations in the slope of the floor. The kennel needs to be an individual compartment; you do not want any cross over of water or urine from one kennel to another. To try and seal small gaps under the frame with mastic compounds is a poor substitute for a well designed kennel. It is prone to damage, breaking down, being chewed and clawed and will require remedial works in a few years' time.

📖 <u>I cannot over emphasise how important it is to ensure that there are no gaps at low level</u>, apart from the hygiene aspects, there is a safety issue (*I have been witness to a litter of well grown alsatian puppies, who managed to pull the tail of another alsatian under the dividing partition of an adjoining kennel; they chewed the tail off*).

The standard method of constructing division walls is to use solid concrete blocks, either to 2000mm high or to 1200mm high then use a metal framed weldmesh/meshlite panel above. The use of metal framed panels with either solid board on the lower sections and glass or meshlite (translucent plastic with metal strengthening) above 1200mm high does tend to open up the building to give the impression of space and airiness.

Sliding hatches

The CIEH insist that new kennels have a sleeping area with a run attached, allowing the dog to have access to either section. This is provided by the use of a sliding hatch or 'pop-hole'. In the past sliding hatches were constructed using a single sheet of galvanised metal.

This has the same disadvantages as using metal for the partitions, it is also a poor insulator from the cold and is extremely noisy, particularly when a dog is scratching it.

A better alternative is to use either a double skin system using two sheets of metal with an inner core of insulation, this will provide better insulation and help reduce noise levels.

The use of Trespa Metion or Perstorp Compact give excellent results in terms of noise reduction and either can be sandwiched with an inner core of insulation to help improve thermal efficiency.

The size of the sliding hatch is partly dictated by the type and size of dog in your care, obviously for boarding and welfare kennels a compromise has to be made. As a guide, I use two sizes of hatch and I have found that these are sufficient for all but the giant breeds of dog.

The sizes are:

650mm wide x 750mm high
650mm wide x 900mm high

For the giant breeds it is extremely useful to have at least one or two kennels which have either a larger sliding hatch to suit the breed or a stable door type arrangement.

In addition to the sliding hatch, a useful extra is the installation of clear PVC strips on the exercise run face of the pop-hole. These strips are extremely beneficial in terms of draught reduction and heat loss. Ideally, the strips should be removable in order to prevent their early demise by a destructive dog.

The final point to consider when designing your kennels is to provide a step or sill between the sleeping area and the exercise run. This will prevent wash-down water creeping into one or other of the compartments.

Sleeping beds

Often the owner will have a preference for a particular type or style. The normal methods used are brick/ block-work and built-in as a raised section off the floor, plastic, glass fibre, metal framed, free standing or fixed and hinged to the wall.

Whichever style you choose, its aim is to provide a sleeping area that the dog feels secure in; it gives protection from draughts, can be easily cleaned, is not too heavy for the staff to lift and remove for cleaning purposes and dries quickly.

As a general guide, larger charities prefer the plastic or glass fibre types as they feel that these offer the dog a better environment and fulfil all of the above criteria.

The hinged, wall fixed platform beds available have lost favour due to the fact that the dog cannot squeeze into a corner as it can with a traditional bed; this obviously reduces the feeling of security.

The older style beds with metal frames tend to be noisy, heavy for the staff and have angles that make them more difficult to clean.

Helpful Hints –

📖 Kennel doors - Most doors are approximately 800mm wide and open inwards. This is a good compromise for ease of access without being too large, making it unmanageable and difficult when manoeuvring large dogs in and out.

📖 Ensure that a small gap is left under the front door panel, approximately 5mm, so that wash down water can run freely into the drainage channel.

📖 When fixing doorframes into brickwork, particularly 100mm thick, ensure that the frame is measured to fix into the centre of the wall to prevent crumbling or damage to the bricks.

📖 Sliding hatch. This is normally fixed onto the outer exercise run wall, directly opposite the counter balance weight to ensure a smooth operation. However, it is easy to install an angled pulley to allow the hatch to be fixed in the most convenient place.

📖 Ensure that the sleeping section of the kennel has sufficient floor space to allow for beds, bowls etc. This can be improved by siting the sliding hatch opposite the main kennel door. By siting the door and sliding hatch in line, it will allow a free corner area where the bed can be positioned.

📖 Install a small number of kennels with mesh tops; this will prevent the loss of a dog over the top of the kennel.

📖 If you decide to use concrete blocks to 1200mm high, with a mesh panel above. It is worth fitting some kennels with translucent meshlite panels. This will act as a solid barrier between the kennels to prevent dominant or aggressive dogs from disturbing their neighbours. Ideally these should be sited at the first or last kennels in the block; this utilises the solid wall of the building, saves money and also provides a more isolated kennel.

📖 Be careful if you have a tiled floor in your kennels and heavy metal framed wall fixed beds. If these are accidentally dropped, the tiles could be damaged!

3.9   KENNEL LIGHTING

Lighting is a major use of electricity, second only to water and space heating. Therefore consideration should be given to the type and amount installed with provision for flexibility.

Clearly, the amount of natural daylight entering the building can have a marked effect on the amount of artificial lighting required.

Whatever form of lighting is provided, this has to be adequate for safe and effective working at any time of the day or night.

Recent advances in lighting technology can give energy savings of approximately 30%, especially when compared to installations over ten years old.

NOTE –   **Lighting is measured in Lux (Lux = One lumen per sq. metre)**
Daylight Factor = Amount of natural daylight admitted through
a window or rooflight

It is generally considered that for dogs a lighting level is required of approximately 200 lux during 12/14 hours of light/day with a 4% D.F. (daylight factor).

For other locations the following levels are recommended:

- Offices -   400 Lux
- Receptions -   200 Lux
- Stairs and corridors -   100 Lux

Internal lighting
Of all systems available, fluorescent tubes are regarded as being the most suitable for the kennel environment. They range from 1200mm to 2400mm and come in either single or double fittings, are low maintenance, cost effective with an operating life of 5000-15000 hours.

Double kennel illustrating engineering brick walls, granolithic screed and central drainage channel.

Above kennel following refurbishment with ceramic tiles, coving and new metalwork.

Note the use of Trespa Metion for the floor channel.

Tiles by Pilkington's

Metalwork by Croft Engineering

Kennel showing the use of smooth tiles in the sleeping area and textured in the corridor.

Tiles by Pilkington's

Drainage system by ACO

Epoxy floor with 50mm coved skirting.

Note the use of acoustic ceiling and bar system instead of mesh for the kennel fronts.

Metalwork by Croft Engineering

Kennel division wall with 6mm meshlite top section.

Metalwork by Croft Engineering

Kennel sleeping area with heavy duty acrylated paint to the lower section and masonry paint above.

Tiles by Architectural Ceramics

Divisional wall - although this has been used for a cattery the materials, Trespa Metion, and Meshlite are highly suitable for kennels.

Metalwork by Croft Engineering

A basic building using colours and textures to improve the aesthetics and ease of management.

Metalwork by Croft Engineering

Double kennel block with covered exercise runs.

Internal view of exercise runs to above building, showing Aco drainage gratings lifted for cleaning, also shows translucent and solid roof covering.

Metalwork by Croft Engineering.

Covered exercise run using block walls to lower section.

Close up view of above exercise run showing roof construction.

A basic kennel block showing use of colours and simple landscaping.

Note – The external colour was a Planning Condition imposed by the local authority.

Covered exercise runs and corridor.

Note the use of block paviours which give a durable and aesthetic finish.

Internal view of old kennel building showing central drainage channel, floor tiles and tiles to lower sections of kennel walls.

Metalwork by Croft Engineering.

Resin floor screed with Aco drainage channel.

Note – The channel has been positioned to allow for the covering.

Helpful Hints -

📖 If you specify fluorescent tubular lighting, it is well worth spending a little extra to purchase the dust/vapour proof, enclosed unit. Apart from being easier to clean, this type of unit will withstand being splashed by over enthusiastic staff using hosepipes.

📖 Change to the new smaller 26mm diameter tubes; the older 38mm are approximately 8% more expensive to run. The new 26mm tubes will fit into your existing holders without modification.

📖 Replace existing starters with new electronic units, these ensure a flicker-free start-up and reduce wear on the tubes.

📖 Fluorescent fittings with high frequency ballast are the most efficient. Although more expensive to buy, they have energy cost savings of around 15%.

3.10 ROOF COVERINGS

In kennels, like domestic houses, the light comes through rooflights and high level windows; the use of low-level windows in the kennel area is not a practical proposition.

The traditional and recommended way of providing daylight to the working area of industrial units and warehouses was to install translucent sheeting or glass to the middle third of each slope on symmetrical pitched roofs and the whole of the north facing slopes.

The advantages of economy in the use of natural lighting from rooflights has to be balanced against the disadvantages of poor thermal and sound insulation, solar heat gain and the fire hazards associated with the materials used. However, the rooflight should be of sufficient area (4% DF for dogs) to provide suitable and adequate daylight to give a uniformity to the working area.

Natural daylight, heating, artificial lighting and ventilation are all an integral part of the kennel design, each dependent upon each other.

Kennels with excessive areas of single glazed rooflighting can give rise to higher levels of solar gain during the summer months than kennels with only small areas of rooflighting.

The CIEH suggest that the kennel temperature should be a minimum of **10°C** and a maximum of **26°C.** Clearly over the past few years we have experienced temperatures reaching the maximum for prolonged periods during the summer months.

Cautionary Note
Once the ambient temperature reaches these high levels, older, poorly insulated, badly ventilated buildings with large areas of single glazed rooflighting will be noticeably affected, often resulting in highly distressed dogs or even worse.

Kennel Roof Materials

Slate and Tile

Traditionally, roofs on smaller kennel buildings were constructed using either slates or concrete tiles and this is still the standard practice. The coverings are fixed onto timber roof trusses or purlins with pitches of at least 25° to the horizontal.

The covering materials are generally poor insulators against transfer of heat. This problem has been overcome by the use of insulating materials such as glass fibre matting and expanded PVC, the insulation is laid between the ceiling joists.
This insulating layer will act to reduce the heat loss from the building to the roof space and also reduce the heat gain from the roof space into the building.

Profiled sheet coverings

The advantage of steel as a material for roof covering is its favourable strength to weight ratio and ductility, make it both practical and economic to use. The other main advantage of this type of covering is the lower pitches that it can be laid at, i.e. 5°. The roof construction is normally a sandwich construction with the insulating material between the outer top sheet and an inner lining sheet.

The sheets come in many styles, profiles, materials and most importantly, colours. Most have a life span in excess of forty years with the major manufacturers giving a thirty-year guarantee.

Sheet materials

- **Hot-dipped galvanised -**This is a method of applying a coating of zinc to the sheet as a protective barrier against the elements. The disadvantage of this sheet is that it is only available in one finished colour, i.e. silver/grey, this tones down over a period of time to a dark grey.

- **Plastic coated -** Most plastic coated steel sheets look very much the same. However, the quality of the coating and the types of coating vary enormously and this results in varying life spans and costs. It is important to realise the type of coating the sheet has.

  The coating serves two purposes; it provides an additional protective barrier and also introduces a wide range of colours to the standard sheets. The effects of ultra-violet radiation will gradually bleach the pigment in the coating over a period of years.

- **Cement sheets** - Often, incorrectly referred to, as asbestos roof sheeting. The sheets are made from a mixture of natural fibres with alternating layers of cement and water. The wet mixture is then rolled flat or formed into corrugated sheets and steam cured to harden it. These cement sheets are used extensively for agricultural, storage and industrial buildings. During recent years the introduction of colour coatings has improved the aesthetic quality of this system and made it more acceptable as a form of roof covering for smaller buildings.

Note - Cement sheets once contained asbestos fibres. However, since March 1998, all new, British made roofing sheets are asbestos-free. The use of asbestos is now illegal.

Sheets manufactured before this date will contain approximately 12% of white asbestos. This point should be taken into consideration if demolitions have to be undertaken.

If asbestos is discovered, then expert advice should be sought, this will take into account the Health & Safety aspect and the legal requirement for the removal and disposal.

Exercise Run Covering

All materials used for, i.e. glass and flat or profiled, transparent or translucent sheets, are used to obtain the maximum transmission of light but offer little resistance to the transmission of sound or heat.

The main systems used for rooflights to the exercise runs are:

- **Glass** - This is the traditional material for rooflights. If you look at most old industrial buildings, it is almost certain that glass sheet fixed in metal frames was the system used.

  Glass has poor mechanical strength and therefore requires the strength of metal glazing bars, set comparatively close together. Today, the main use of glass is for smaller, preformed dormer type double glazed window units.

Profiled sheet

- **UPVC -** This is one of the cheapest of the translucent plastic materials used for rooflights. It has reasonable light transmission (77%), reasonable impact and scratch resistance. On exposure to solar gain it has a useful life expectancy of around twenty-five years. However, it will discolour with age to give a yellow/brown colour. Over this period the light transmission will be markedly reduced.

- **GRP - glass reinforced polyester -** Is similar to UPVC in terms of appearance, impact resistance and strength, however it does not have the light transmittance of UPVC, with only 50%-70%.

- **Polycarbonate -** Is manufactured as single, double or triple wall systems. It has good light transmittance (88%), is extremely strong, durable and has good weathering qualities. It is the most expensive of the plastic materials used and is often used in situations where glass would be damaged. Its main use is in domestic conservatories and is available in either clear of bronzed tint finish. The installation of a twin/triple wall system with a bronzed tint will help reduce solar gain and provide a more controllable working environment. It is highly useful for the kennel environment.

Obviously the roof structure to the main kennel building, i.e. the central sleeping area, needs to be fully insulated to prevent condensation and heat loss during the winter and solar gain during the summer. The roof structures for most kennel buildings consist mainly of solid roof materials, i.e. tiles or profiled sheet with the inclusion of a few velux rooflights to allow some natural light in.

However, it is the exercise run roof covering, whether this is an integral part of the building as used by most charities or a free-standing structure as is the norm for most boarding kennels, that tends to be the area of concern to most kennel owners.

Because of the general use of single skin products, the extremes of weather are most noticeable in the exercise runs, i.e. too hot during the summer or too wet/cold during the winter. Generally the problems associated with high temperatures are more difficult to correct than those with low temperatures.

The materials and methods of construction vary tremendously and are dependent upon several factors, i.e. finances, proximity of neighbours, geographical location.

The methods I have seen used are:

1. Single sheet solid material, i.e. metal/cement roof sheet
2. Single skin transparent GRP type material
3. Part solid and part translucent sheeting
4. Twinwall system
5. Twin sheet system with the inclusion of insulation

1. Single Solid Sheet

Advantages
- Cost effective.
- Easy installation.

Disadvantages
- Can be affected by extremes of temperature in certain locations, see section 3.2 of roof sheet U'Values.
- Metal sheeting increases noise reverberation times.
- Can make the kennels dark in certain locations.

2. Single sheet translucent sheeting

Advantages
- Cost effective.
- Easy installation.

Disadvantages
- Can be affected by extremes of temperature in certain locations.
- Does not provide any shady areas for the dog to lie in.

3. Part solid - part translucent

Advantages
- Cost effective.
- Easy installation.
- Provides shade for the dog.
- Is generally an acceptable form of covering for most situations.

Disadvantages
- Can be affected by extremes of temperature in certain locations.

4. Polycarbonate Twinwall System

Advantages
- Relatively easy installation.
- Excellent insulator and will provide protection from solar gain, particularly sheeting with a bronzed tint finish.
- Extremely strong and durable.

Disadvantages
- Expensive to install, approximately £30 for a sheet of twinwall, 10mm thick at 3000mm long x 900mm wide.

5. Twin sheet system with insulation

Advantages
- Excellent insulator providing protection from solar gain.
- The lining sheet can be a waterproof board, i.e. masterboard with the insulation sandwiched between the lining and top sheet or an acoustic board/tile forming a false ceiling. This will help reduce the noise levels within the exercise runs as well as providing protection from solar gain.
- The acoustic board system will not only provide insulation from the sun but also help reduce and muffle some of the noise from the dogs' barking.

Disadvantages
- Expensive to install.

General Guidance - My preferred option is to install a combination of translucent and solid sheeting with an acoustic board under the solid portion of the roof. As a general rule, I would recommend covering approximately 33% of the roof with translucent sheeting.

Helpful Hints –

📖 If you have existing kennels with large areas of translucent sheeting and experience problems with excessive heat during the summer months, then you need to take action. The normal method is to paint over some of the rooflights with a white or solar reflective paint. Although this is only a temporary measure, it will rectify a major problem for a short while. A more expensive measure is either to replace some of the sheeting with solid/insulated boarding or to spray/paint one of the specialist alkyd resin products over the top.

3.11   KENNEL HEATING SYSTEMS

The CIEH recommend a kennel temperature of between 10°C - 26°C.
Depending on the size of the building, its insulation qualities and the time of the year
it is in use, all of these factors will affect the type of heating system you install.

The decision on what type of heating system to install into the kennel building needs
to be taken at an early date; it is often dictated by the services available locally, i.e.
mains gas.

On older properties the heating is often one of the last items to be upgraded,
frequently relying totally on infrared heat lamps or the odd floor standing electric fan
heater. It is not always the cost of upgrading these systems that prevents the work
from being carried out; often it can be the problem of choosing the most suitable
system.

The systems I have seen in use in a variety of premises are:

1. Infrared Heat Lamps.
2. Electric Fan Heaters.
3. Quart Halogen Heaters.
4. Night Storage Heaters.
5. Boiler Fired High Level Fan Convectors.
6. Domestic Radiators or Tubular Heating Pipes.
7. Underfloor Heating (electric and wet system).
8. Solar Energy.
9. Air Conditioning.
10. Heat Recovery.

Whichever system is used must be convenient, have a suitable service back up, be
cost effective and easy to use. It is pointless having a complicated system that the
staff are afraid of, or do not understand.

It is also worth considering the amount of use the heaters will receive; if for an
isolated building only used for a few weeks a year, then an expensive boiler fired
heating system will not be the most cost effective or suitable.

The key word is 'flexibility'- choose the system that is right for your requirements
and level of use.

1. Infrared heat lamps

This system uses several types of bulb; such as red heat bulbs, ceramic heat lamps and dull emitter bulbs. Since the heat is radiant, the animals feel the warmth immediately. All have been around for a long time and are still extremely popular; they are used for cats, dogs, poultry and particularly pigs. The infrared rays given off are similar to those given off by the sun.

The system is relatively cheap to install; simple to use and cost effective when used in small numbers. The lamps are designed to provide a direct heat over the animal; they do not provide an effective level of warmth to the building or room. Most charities tend to use them as a backup to the main heating system for young or frail dogs.

If you choose to install this system, ensure that you use the ceramic or dull emitters, they are far safer and stronger than the red bulb variety, which tend to explode when splashed with water. *All electrically operated equipment needs to be correctly installed at high level, out of the dogs' reach and to have a suitably protected electrical supply.*

2 Electric fan heaters

Unlike infrared heaters, an electric fan convector is suitable for room heating, particularly for large areas. The industrial varieties come in a range of powers from 2kw to 25kw. They are usually wall or ceiling mounted, simple to use, normally come with a built-in thermostat and provide instant heat.

The disadvantage of these units is the cost of running them; four heaters at 6kw each equates to an hourly running figure of around £1.44 per hour at six pence per unit; clearly this is extremely expensive. However, for kennels only used intermittently they are highly suitable.

3 Quartz Halogen heaters

These units are often specified where there is a need for localised heat or immediate, all over warmth. They are commonly used in industrial and commercial applications in premises that are lightly constructed, naturally cold and have poor insulation. They are also used in large buildings, which only need to have a small area of it heated. They normally come in 1.5kw-4.5kw loading per unit.

The same warnings apply to all forms of electric heating used in a potentially wet or damp environment; they require to be correctly installed by a qualified electrician and have suitably protected circuits.

4 Night storage heaters

A modern night storage heater is a slim, often not more than 170mm deep, efficient form of room heating. These appliances are cost effective, being charged during the night on cheaper electricity; controllable and correctly sized they can give off high levels of heat.

For certain applications they are highly recommended, e.g. staff rooms, rooms that house perishable goods that need to be kept damp free. They can be used in the kennel environment providing you can raise them off the floor by approximately 300mm, to prevent water and urine from corroding them.

The main disadvantage associated with them in the kennel environment is that during the early evening when it starts to get cold the heaters are losing their heating capacity; they will not be recharged until after 12.30am.

Without any additional form of heating, this could lead to kennels being too cold for a period of time.

5. Boiler fired high level fan convectors

These units are normally found in industrial units, warehouses and large areas that require a good level of heating. Unlike electrical fan convectors, these units require a boiler, either gas or oil fired as they operate on high temperature hot water.

They have a finned tubular heating element with a fan to improve the circulation of warm air. *(I have seen this style of heater in operation for over twenty years and they have proved to be extremely reliable and durable)*

In addition to providing heat they can also be used during the summer months as a cooling fan. The important point to remember when specifying such units is to check the level of noise they produce when working; you require the quietest unit available.

Some people are concerned about the possibility of dust, germs being blown through the building with this type of system. I have not found this to be problem.

6. Domestic radiators

Most modern panel radiators are constructed using light gauge steel pressing welded together, although heavy cast iron units are available; they are used extensively in homes and offices. Radiators, like boiler fired fan convectors require some form of boiler to provide the necessary hot water for them to operate.

An alternative to radiators is tubular heating pipes, these are normally 50mm diameter and extremely durable. They have the disadvantage of being not particularly aesthetically pleasing.
The other concern is if they are mounted at low level, there is a risk of dogs trapping their legs behind the pipes if they do not have a protective cage over them.

It is normal practice to install radiators at low level, as in a domestic house. However, this is not always practical in the kennel environment due to narrow corridors, problems associated with rusting, kennel design and layout etc. An option is to fix them at high level above the sleeping area. Although this is not as efficient as a low-level installation, it is still highly suitable.

The merits of radiant heat are:

- Radiant heat gives a greater feeling of warmth with a lower air temperature; this achieves about a 15% saving in fuel costs.

- Radiant heat does not heat the air through which it passes, but heats solid objects on which it falls, i.e. walls and floors. These warm surfaces set up convection currents, which reduce the heat loss from the human or animal by convection.

7.   Underfloor heating (electric and wet system)

Electric

Underfloor heating has a higher capital cost than most other forms of electric heating; however correctly installed, it should last for many years without requiring to have any remedial works carried out on it.

This system normally comes as sealed pads of varying sizes or lengths of insulated cable laid to the required areas. The low running costs make them highly cost effective, with the option to select small areas where the heat is required.

If you plan to install such a system, ensure that you have detailed drawings of the areas covered by the cables or pads. This might be extremely useful for the any future works that might be carried out, particularly if fixing new metalwork to the floor; however it can be traced with the use of a metal detector.

Wet system

It was during the 1960's that underfloor heating became popular for a short while using copper and steel pipes with hot water running through them, from an oil/gas fired boiler.

This system did not last for long; it proved to be unreliable, difficult to maintain and had to be run at extremely high temperatures, particularly with poorly insulated buildings.

Since then it has evolved a long way with the use of polyethylene and aluminium pipes and better insulated homes. It is still not as popular as in some countries, for example in Switzerland, 80% of homes have underfloor heating and over 35% in Germany.

The benefits of this system are:
- Aesthetically pleasing, with no obvious source of heater.
- Low running costs, with savings of over 15% compared with radiator systems.
- Gives an even temperature throughout the room and helps dry the floor extremely quickly.

Helpful Hints –

🕮 If underfloor heating is installed try to leave approximately 30% of the kennel sleeping area free of heating. This allows the dog some freedom to choose either a warm area or slightly cooler if it wants.

8. Solar Energy

Although I haven't seen this used for kennels, there is no reason why it should not be. It has certainly gained prominence for the domestic market and is normally associated with providing hot water.

Like all things, the cost of installation has to be weighed against the potential savings.

A conventional system uses solar collectors, through which water is circulated, heated and then piped to a well insulated storage tank. The solar panels are normally sited on the roof of the building although they can be mounted in any convenient location.

9. Air conditioning

This is a system that is little used for single storey kennels. However, it is used in animal hospitals and large multi-storey kennels such as Battersea Dogs' Home. These buildings tend to be closed environments and totally sealed from the outside or where there is a noise problem.

Air conditioning comprises filtration, heating, ventilation, cooling and dehumidification by mechanical means; it is generally more controllable and able to adapt to the climatic changes than conventional domestic heating systems. It is a modular system and can incorporate all of the elements mentioned or only some of them, i.e. comfort cooling and heating.

Although these systems are extremely efficient, and will provide a good working environment in terms of humidity, warmth, cooling and comfort; they are expensive to install and maintain.

These systems require a higher level of maintenance than one would normally associate with kennels and require specialist engineers to maintain them.

For normal welfare kennels I would not advocate their use and would look at the simpler systems mentioned above.

10.   Heat recovery

For smaller buildings the installation of a heat recovery unit can be extremely beneficial, not only will it reduce your heating costs, it will also act as a ventilation and humidity control unit as well.

These small units are a basic form of air-conditioning, readily available off the shelf and do not have the high costs and complications associated with a purpose designed system.

A heat recovery unit is a self-contained unit with a built-in heat exchanger; they are extremely efficient and will recover up to 70% of the heat from the building.

The basic principal of the unit is that wet warm air is drawn over a heat exchange block, whilst fresh external air is drawn across in the opposite direction.

Separate airflows ensure that no cross contamination takes place, they can be either a single room unit or a larger unit, which will be able to cope with several rooms.

3.12 VENTILATION

The purpose of ventilation is to remove high concentrations of body odours, carbon dioxide and water vapours, dust and excess heat from the room. The stale air in the room is replaced with fresh and this creates air movement; giving the feeling of freshness without *draughts*.

Ventilation can be achieved by either natural or mechanical means. It is generally accepted that for kennels with full occupancy, a level of air changes per hour should be between 8-10.
The more controllable and uniform this is the better the results will be.

The normal systems used are:

Natural ventilation
Is provided by open windows, doors and sliding hatches. It is dependent on the wind and air temperatures, i.e. warm air rises, which creates a stack effect. If there is no wind and the temperature inside the building is at the same temperature as the outside, natural ventilation will be non-existent.

The utilisation of the 'stack effect' is well known and is exploited in operations that generally have consistent high internal temperatures such as poultry houses and foundries.   Due its lack of control it has little to offer the kennel owner.

Natural inlet with mechanical extract
This is the most common type of system used for kitchens, workshops, etc.
The extractor fan creates negative pressure on its inlet side, this causes the air inside the room to move toward the fan, which is then displaced by fresh air coming from outside.

This is probably the most widely used system in kennels; it is cost effective, simple to use, can be controlled and will remove odours and condensation.

Mechanical inlet and natural extract
Fresh air is impelled into the building, thereby creating a pressure, the contaminated air is expelled by natural seepage through windows, sliding hatches, etc. If this system is installed, it is preferential that the air is either heated before it is forced into the building or at least directed away from the sleeping area to prevent draughts.

Mechanical inlet and extract

This system offers the greatest degree of control; it is the most expensive and is used in cinemas, offices and particularly operating theatres. The air is normally filtered and the warm extracted air can be recirculated in order to save fuel costs.

For offices, etc a slight pressurisation of the air inside the building is achieved by using an extract fan smaller than the inlet fan.

However in kennels this system does not work particularly efficiently due to the sliding hatches being open for extended periods.

Helpful Hints -

📖 As a general guide, the installation of natural inlet with mechanical extract is the normal standard for most kennels. Instead of having a few small window/wall fan units, I would suggest the use of large acoustic fan/s or heat recovery units for smaller buildings; these are normally mounted in the roof void, linked to a ducted system with extract ports over the sleeping area.

This gives a uniform level of ventilation to the entire building, rather than only a few areas. It also gives a fully controllable system, allowing a trickle system if required, with extremely quiet fans.

3.13 CONDENSATION (Dehumidification)

I will say from the outset that I believe that most kennels are too wet or damp.

The reasons for this are straightforward, i.e. water from cleaning processes, damp blankets and bedding and dogs that have had access to uncovered runs when it has been raining. All of these factors contribute to a poor environment in which to house animals; a damp environment is a healthy breeding place for viruses, like kennel cough.

Condensation is a problem that affects many kennels, businesses and domestic homes. It is particularly noticeable during the winter months, and at night, when the temperature falls, the humidity rises and condensation forms; your bathroom window is a good indicator of the problem.

If you run a hot bath on a cold day it will not be long before the inside of the window is heavy with running water. The air we breathe is like a big sponge; the warmer the air the more water in the form of vapour it can absorb. As soon as the air is cooled for any reason it contracts and has to unload its absorbed water onto the cold surface, this is condensation or (dew).

The materials used in modern kennelling are not the most beneficial to counter this problem; the cold, hard finishes of tiles or sealed blockwork readily show the problem. In older kennels constructed of timber, the problem was not so noticeable; timber being warmer to the touch and therefore able to hold more vapour.
The vapour was still there and became absorbed into the timber; an ideal place for germs and bacteria to breed.

To combat the problems associated with condensation requires a specialist engineers advice in relation to *your* building. Heating, ventilation, humidity should be looked at as a whole and not as isolated problems; approaching the problem in this manner should give excellent results.

If heating and ventilation alone do not correct the problem of condensation you are then faced with two choices.

These are:

1. Dehumidification

These simple units can be of great advantage to the kennel owner and are used extensively for drying new houses, basement cellars and for keeping document stores dry. They come in a range of sizes and extraction levels to suit the application, they are cost effective, give excellent results and are simple to operate and maintain.

The basic principle of the system is that moist air within the building is drawn over a heater coil ensuring it deposits its condensed water, which is then drained away. During this process the latent energy of the water vapour is recovered and is recycled back into the air as it leaves the unit. This warmed air can be a useful source of heating for the kennel. Correctly sized, a dehumidifier will reduce your heating and ventilation costs and at the same time improves the kennel environment by removing excess moisture from the air.

2. Building Construction & Management Technique

The provision of increased heating, ventilation, insulation and/or an improvement in the construction of the building, a revision of your management techniques.

3.14 ACOUSTIC MEASURES (internally & externally)

Internal

Noise is one of the main reasons for complaint to local authorities relating to kennels; this has been particularly noticeable since the **Environmental Protection Act 1995.** The specific points of this Act are dealt with in section five. All kennels have been affected, boarding, breeding, welfare and quarantine to some degree or other. The more dogs you have in your care, generally the greater the problem. External factors will also have an influence on the problem; a large kennel complex close to a built-up area is fraught with potential problems.

The law relating to noise is not unique to the UK. I have met visitors from France and Australia who have been looking at kennel design in the UK and associated problems, particularly in relation to noise. Both centres had one thing in common, a restriction had been placed upon them by the local authority to reduce the noise levels from their kennels.

Unit of noise measurement

The unit of measurement for sound is measured in decibels (dB). The scale for this is logarithmic; this means that 90dB is ten times the intensity of 80dB and a hundred times the intensity of 70dB. An increase of 3dB doubles the sound intensity, so that 87dB is twice as noisy as 84dB. To put this into some context, a normal office environment is approximately 50dB.

Nature of Noise

Sound is the transmission of vibrations at different frequencies; noise is defined as unwanted sound. The ear is a pressure sensitive mechanism, detecting small changes of pressure over a wide range of frequencies; in humans the ear is most sensitive to sounds at frequencies of 1000-5000 cycles per second. This unit of measurement is known as the Hertz (Hz).
Dogs are most sensitive to sounds at frequencies from 500 Hz to 16kHz.

Reverberation Time

This is the time taken for the sound to decay to 60dB. Kennels by their very nature have poor acoustic properties; hard smooth surfaces do not absorb noise, therefore, any noise generated tends to reverberate around the inside of the building. The longer the reverberation time, the more uncomfortable and echoing the building will be.
For offices a comfortable working environment is considered to be 0.4-0.6 seconds, in sports halls and swimming pools this time can be as long as 4-6 seconds.

Noise Levels -

	SOUND LEVEL IN dB	SOUND SOURCE
HARMFUL RANGE	140 130	**Jet engine Industrial riveting hammer**
CRITICAL RANGE	120 117 90	**Propeller aircraft Generator Heavy vehicle**
SAFE RANGE	70 60 50	**Private car Ordinary conversation Ordinary office**

Maximum Exposure

It has already been stated that the levels of noise generated in kennels can be potentially damaging to human hearing, therefore consideration must be given to this issue. In order to control and monitor noise levels a system of "action levels" has been introduced. This system involves three specified levels of noise exposure at which you are duty bound to respond:

LEVEL 1 - Establishes a daily personal noise exposure of 85dB.
LEVEL 2 - Maximum exposure of 90 dB.
LEVEL 3 - This peak action level of 200 pascals is for employees who are exposed to intermittent high noise levels.

If noise levels reach 85 dB the employer must inform his/her employees and issue suitable ear protection. At 90 dB employers must reduce noise where reasonably practicable, ensure that employees have and use ear protection and have designated protection zones.

Note – A Pascal is a measurement of sound pressure. Due to the small scales used i.e. 0 dB = 20 millionths of a Pascal the dB scale is more often used.

Recommended Maximum Exposure without Protection

Average Noise Level	Maximum Exposure in One Working Day
90	8 hours
93	4 hours
96	2 hours
99	1 hour
102	30 minutes
105	15 minutes
108	7.5 minutes
111	3.7 minutes

Studies carried out by the Universities Federation for Animal Welfare (UFAW) studied the nature of noise in kennels and how it can be reduced. They also investigated the problems and potentially damaging effects high noise levels have on dogs in relation to stress and disease.

It is recognised that dogs have far superior hearing than humans; in fact they can detect sounds that are up to four times quieter than the human ear can detect.

Clearly, most people soon realise and accept that these high levels of noise which are potentially harmful to humans will undoubtedly have a detrimental effect on the dogs as well. Therefore action has to be taken to try and reduce these high levels; ideally this should be considered and as much potential noise as possible 'designed out' rather than relying on remedial measures.

From my own studies using a very basic hand held noise level meter, in our larger, older kennels holding 15-20 dogs, I obtained readings of around 100-108 dB; clearly this is unacceptable. In order to try to reduce the overall level we started and are continuing to carry out a programme of improvements and remedial works. This work has taken the form of installing acoustic roof and wall cladding; and in the worst cases total demolition of the building and replacement with better designed kennels.

At one centre the recent installation of an acoustic ceiling resulted in a reduction of approximately 13dB from an average of 108dB to 95dB. Although this is still high and in the critical range, it has appreciably improved and reduced the overall noise intensity and the building has become "tolerable"; with improved kennel management systems we hope to reduce the levels even more.

Noise Abatement Notice

This can be issued at any time by the local authority if it deems the noise levels too high; normally such only investigations would follow a complaint from a neighbour.

Once a complaint has been brought to the attention of the authority, it is duty bound to act upon it; this will take the form of measuring and recording the noise levels; this in itself is not a straightforward task. A report on the levels recorded will be served to the owner/occupier of the premises and is held in a register.

This register is public property and is freely available for anyone to view.

Having established the noise level, the local authority can, if the level is unreasonable, serve a notice under Section 66. This requires a reduction to a specified level, within a stated period of time; this period will not exceed six months. Once served, the owner must take steps to correct and improve the situation and also demonstrate that they have taken steps to provide a long-term solution. Failure to act can result in prosecution or even closure.

Clearly, you must take any noise complaint very seriously; it could potentially be the end of your business. The onus will be on you to show that you have taken all reasonable and practicable steps to reduce the levels and improve the situation.

A serious noise complaint does not just go away!

Practical methods to reduce noise levels

- The installation of an acoustic ceiling and wall baffles will bring significant improvements to the noise levels and reduce reverberation times (ensure that you specify a totally moisture resistant tile if you are installing a lightweight tile system).

- Look at your management systems; minor changes here can help reduce noise e.g. do visitors really need to see all of the dogs, can you provide staff and separate visitor zones?

- Install separation doors into the buildings to try and reduce the amount of disturbance to other areas. Ideally these should be solid, half hour fire resistant doors; these are durable and will help protect the building and animals in the event of a fire.
  These doors should be fitted with an overhead-closing device to ensure that they function as fire doors, this will also help reduce the noise breakout as it is an automatic system and lessens the chances of doors being left open.

- Try to construct partitions between buildings out of solid concrete block; this will help reduce the transmission of noise between sections/buildings.

- Avoid long straight corridors. Linear kennels increase the amount of excitability of the dogs within the building due to them being aware of staff/visitors, but not able to see them.

- Long, straight corridors can act as handrails for noise. As noise travels less effectively round corners, anything that can break-up the flow is advantageous.

- Try to keep ancillary activities separate from the kennel work.

- Change metal feeding bowls for plastic; it is surprising how much noise is generated by dogs pushing bowls around the floor, or by staff dropping a metal bowl.

- Look at the construction of the building. Do you have metal divisions/partitions? These can generate high levels of noise and increase the reverberation times. If you wish to install metal divisions, I believe that the only way to help combat some of the high noise levels produced by this type of finish is to sandwich a layer of polystyrene/polyurethane in between sheets of metal.

🐕 Do you have external exercise runs that face other exercise areas? This can be a major source of noise with dogs able to see each other, particularly if animals are constantly being moved around.

🐕 Change mop buckets to plastic to help reduce noise.

🐕 Do you have noise-producing equipment in the kennel building e.g. boilers, air-conditioning or ventilation fans? Old equipment is not only less efficient than new, it also tends to be noisier.

🐕 On older buildings that have been adapted or are of a poor standard, it might be cheaper and more cost effective in the long term to think about replacing these with new kennels.

Correctly designed and specified, this will go a long way to help resolving your problems. Certainly if you have a serious noise complaint which is being investigated by the local authority, you will have to demonstrate ways in which the situation can be improved.

Acoustic Materials

The installation of acoustic materials to the ceiling and any high level areas will act as highly efficient sound absorbers, i.e. a reduction of sound within the room and a reduction in reverberation times. The other use of acoustic materials is sound attenuation i.e. the reduction of sound travelling from the source to adjacent rooms.

Most of the proprietary ceiling tiles used in the kennel environment use similar materials and construction methods, i.e. a glass wool backing with a decorative microporous surface, laid in a suspended grid. The materials used also increases the insulation within the building.

The more common tiles used are the Hygiene range manufactured by Ecophon, or Parafon Fjord by Armstrong both of these systems have excellent acoustic properties and are highly recommended for use in the kennel environment.

Suspended Ceiling Tiles –

The decisive factors when selecting suitable tiles are:

- A thickness of between 25-40mm.

- A moisture resistance of at least 90%.

- A decorative finish suitable for cleaning with a cloth. Products are available that will withstand cleaning by pressure washing; however these are expensive and are normally reserved for areas requiring high levels of hygiene such as food preparation rooms in commercial suppliers.

- A product that offers higher levels of acoustic control.

- A product with a light coloured finish. The majority of tiles used are white, as this offers the highest level of light reflectance. However, most of the larger manufacturers offer tiles in a limited range of pastel colours.

Wood Wool Slabs

Wood wool cement slabs differ in appearance and construction to lightweight ceiling tiles. Wood wool has been used in the construction industry for many years and are available in either loadbearing or non-load bearing panels. They are manufactured entirely from natural, non-toxic materials and come in panels as large as 4000mm x 600mm x 150mm thick.

The product is used for such applications as roofing, wall panels, machine rooms and for the kennel owner, ceilings. Woodcemair is the trade name of one highly suitable product and is manufactured by Torvale Building Products.

This product has been used by The Guide Dogs for the Blind in their kennels for many years and has proven to be extremely effective at reducing noise.

The main disadvantage with this system is that the only colour available is brown; this is the products' natural colour. However, the aesthetic appearance of the product can be improved with the application of a coat of emulsion paint, without reducing the performance of the material.

The main advantages with this system are:

1. Ease of Installation - Due to the size of the panels available it can be treated like any other board-like material and can be fastened directly to ceiling joists/purlins and at high level on the walls.

2. Acoustic Properties - The acoustic properties of this material are excellent and generally exceed the absorption and attenuation figures of the lightweight glass wool systems. This is primarily due to its thickness, density and weight. The fact is worth remembering if you have a noise problem or a particularly sensitive area.

Helpful Hints –

 If you have a problem site in relation to noise or a building where you want very high levels of acoustic absorption and attenuation, a combination of Woodcemair with a lightweight system below will provide a building which has excellent acoustic properties and is also aesthetically pleasing.

External noise

We have looked at the problems associated with noise from inside the kennel; the same noise will also travel and could result in a complaint under the Environmental Protection Act 1990.

Any noise generated from the kennels will decrease rapidly once it is in the open, the graph shows how rapidly this happens:

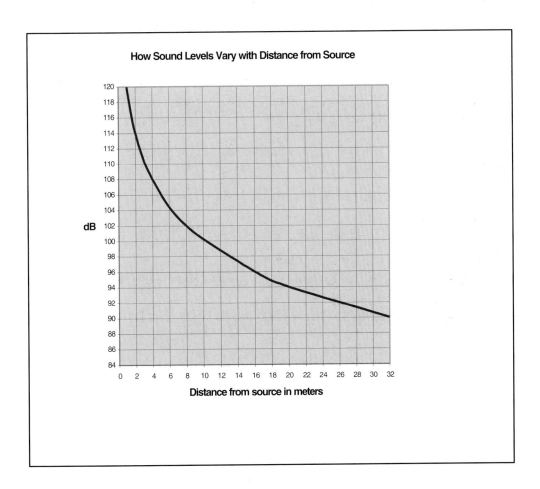

Practical measures to reduce external noise levels

🐕 Site kennels as far away from neighbours as possible.

🐕 Arrange exercise runs so that they do not face other runs.

🐕 Look at installing earth bunds all around the kennels; on new constructions this
🐕 can come from the site excavations. To be effective, the bunding requires to be at least 2.5m high, (tree shelterbelts are not suitable sound barriers). The bunding can then be landscaped to provide an aesthetic, visual barrier for your centre.

🐕 If purchasing a new site, look at the surrounding geography. Is the site in a valley with strong prevailing winds that will carry any noise onto potential neighbours? If so, can you position any non-kennel buildings in between? Although this will not stop the problem totally, it will help.

🐕 Install solid partitions to help prevent from dogs seeing each other and racing up and down the exercise runs.

🐕 If you have full height mesh safety corridors, look at reducing these and building a solid wall to 1000mm high with either mesh panels above or, better still acoustic louvres.

🐕 Install acoustic materials onto the underside of the external exercise runs; this will help absorb some of the noise and provide better shading with cooler exercise runs during the summer.

🐕 Look at your site management techniques. Can you isolate any non-kennel works from other procedures?

🐕 Try to minimise the amount of disturbance to the animals from non- kennel staff.

🐕 Look at planting trees/bushes around the site. Although these will not help to reduce noise levels, they will act as visual barriers to prevent animals from seeing each other, or members of the public walking around the site.

3.15 ANIMAL STRESS & REDUCTION MEASURES

Stress
Stress can be emotional, physical or mental and is caused by situations over which the dog has no control.

Dogs coming into a kennel environment are particularly prone to stress, as they have to cope with a change in environment, are exposed to unfamiliar sounds, foods and routines.

By providing a safe, caring environment that follows a sympathetic but strict routine, most dogs take no more than 3 days to settle in, after that they become less anxious and more secure.

Symptoms of stress
Stress can manifest itself in a number of ways. The dog's behaviour may change, he may refuse to eat or allow himself to be handled, he may withdraw mentally, or he may become aggressive or show overly submissive behaviour.
Other indications of stress in kennels are excessive panting, yawning or repetitive behaviour such as pacing or staring at the wall.
Prolonged stress can also lead to the immune system failing to fight infections, weight loss, irritability and depression.

Ability to cope with stress
Some dogs, like people, are much more prone to suffering from stress.
Generally, if the dog is brought up as a well socialised animal that has been exposed to a wide variety of situations as a young dog, he will cope much better with change.

Even well-socialised pet dogs may find the contrast between home life with lots of attention and the institutional aspects of the boarding kennel, however well run, difficult to cope with. This is especially true of quarantine kennels where dogs have to spend extended times in isolation, which can lead to the development of stereotypic behaviours.

Rescue and rehoming centres have to be particularly aware of stress related problems as many dogs in rescue centres are there because they have not been properly socialised in the first place. Therefore, the dogs that cope least well are the very ones that are likely to end up in stressful environments. However, whether you are running kennels, pet boarding, quarantine or unwanted "rescue" dogs - broad rules still apply.

Much can be done to reduce stress in kennel dogs by carefully considering the physical environment and by the actual kennel routine. However, none of this is a replacement for skilled, competent and sympathetic staff.

Reducing Stress

Admitting dogs into kennels
As much information as possible about the dog should be sought. Diet, behaviour around strangers, children, dogs and other animals, etc. are all-important factors that will affect his handling and placement in kennels. The dog's favourite toys and bedding (or an old towel with the owners scent on it) placed in his kennel will make it a less hostile and more familiar place.

Noise
Dogs have sensitive hearing – and effective sound control/ absorption (see section 3.14) is essential to avoid stressful noise levels.

Visual Barriers
Visual barriers between some dogs will be necessary – whilst many more may enjoy being able to see each other. Some, especially shy or nervous animals, will need the extra privacy and protection of their space that is provided by having a partial wall, or solid panel area to the front of the kennel, rather than totally open mesh or bar.

Small Units
Smaller units not only reduce noise but also help the dogs to become familiar with those sharing the same block. Having small units of 10 or less dogs not only helps reduce noise but also means the dogs get to know who is sharing the block with them.

Dogs, like people, are more comfortable if they know those sharing the same area. Smaller units also enable the staff to get to know the dogs and it is easier to know which dogs to place next to each other.

Placement of dogs

The employment of experienced staff is very important to the care of the dogs. By placing shy dogs near more confident (not aggressive) dogs, the shy dogs can become more confident at approaching the front of the kennel to greet people.

Dogs that are aggressive towards other dogs should always be placed at the end of a run of kennels, so that they can be taken out without having to go past all the other dogs. If dogs are housed in the kennel next to them, the partition should be solid so that the aggressive dog can neither visually intimidate nor physically make contact with the dog next to him.

Handling

Ideally dogs in kennels should be handled as much as possible. This is especially important when the dogs may have to stay for extended periods; otherwise they can lose their tolerance and interest in people.

Handling also helps dogs used to a lot of attention to adjust to the kennel environment. In addition to daily walking and regular grooming, dogs can be petted and spoken to as kennel staff go about their daily routine, i.e. feeding, picking up in the runs, locking up at night, etc.

Because of the limited human contact in kennels, dogs quickly learn how to gain attention from humans passing through the kennels. Kennels where dogs are shouted at for barking, or where staff shout at and push dogs down when they jump up will be characterised by dogs who bark continually and leap up and down at staff and visitors. This adds to the general noise levels and stress of the whole establishment (dogs, staff and visitors).

Kennels will have "noise peaks" such as feeding times, but otherwise should be quiet. This is achieved by predictable routines. Staff should also only interact with the dogs when they are quiet and wait for the dogs to stop jumping up at the door before going in to clip the lead on for a walk.

Mixing dogs in runs/ kennels

Unless dogs come into kennels together and get on well, it is advisable not to mix them. Increased risk of disease, fights and becoming more dog than people-orientated are all potential problems. The only exception might be in rescue kennels where dogs are kept on a permanent basis. There, the companionship of another dog, especially where staff time is limited, is necessary, although this should not be a replacement for human contact and play.

Kennel routine

Dogs need routine - the more predictable the routine, the less anxious the dog will be. So the time the dog is fed, walked and handled are all better kept to a predictable and regular schedule.

Feeding

Where possible the dog should be kept on the diet he is accustomed to and any change of diet should be introduced gradually. Ideally, feed twice daily and feed a good low bulk diet.

Smaller quantities of a highly digestible food fed regularly are less stressful on the dogs' digestive system. By feeding more than once a day the dog has an additional pleasant experience to look forward to.

Restrict visiting time

Strangers looking around are very stressful as they invade the dogs' space and often interact inappropriately by staring and bending over the dogs. At least a one or two hour break from visitors, mid day should be provided.

This routine should be strictly adhered to so that the dogs can be confident that their rest will not be interrupted or their space invaded.

Environment enrichment

The provision of chew toys, especially suspended toys, encourages the dogs to play. Various boxes and platforms at different heights for the dogs to lie on or jump on and off, tunnels and large balls all add to variety and mental stimulation for the dog.

The more the dog can be occupied, especially in physical activity, the lower his stress levels will be.

3.16 KENNEL DRAINAGE SYSTEMS

All new kennels should have efficient drainage systems; this should include both the internal sleeping area and the external exercise area. Most local authorities and the Environmental Agency will not allow any form of wash down water to naturally seep into the ground; it requires to be channelled into an approved drainage system.

The choice of whether to install a single central corridor gully or two, one in front of the sleeping area either side of the corridor is up to the individual. It usually depends on available finances and the type of kennels you operate; a grated channel system can cost in the region of £60.00 per linear metre.

In double-banked kennels the twin system has the advantage of keeping the corridor dry and free from urine, wash down water, etc. The other main consideration is, if you choose a single channel down the centre of the building, it will be far safer to install a grated system; this will prevent staff/visitors slipping into the channel.

The more common systems used are:

1. Proprietary preformed polymer/concrete channels with a choice of suitable gratings.
2. Ceramic channel tiles.
3. Open channel system.

1. Preformed channels

The benefits of using a complete drainage system make for an easy, trouble free system. The most common material used is polymer concrete - this is light in weight and has a smooth internal surface; this helps prevent a build-up of sediment, it comes in pre-sloped sections and is resistant to most acids and dilute alkalis.

The more popular ranges come with a variety of suitable gratings from pedestrian weights right up to units suitable for airports. They are inherently safe with secure, lockable gratings if required and will handle a large volume of water without it splashing and swilling all over the floor, *(this system is often used by the larger charities)*.

The only disadvantage with a grated system is that some people are concerned that it is a potential area for germs/bacteria to build up. However, with correct kennel management and hygiene controls this should not be a problem; it is however slightly more time consuming to lift and clean the gratings.

2.   Ceramic dished channel

Clearly if you have a tiled floor, the obvious answer is to install a complementary channel tiled system. The major manufacturers all provide suitable systems with the necessary sections i.e. stopends, corners etc. The range of colours does tend to be limited.

The system when correctly installed, is extremely durable, aesthetically pleasing and hygienic. The only problem I have found with these channel tiles is the shallowness of the dish; it is only 20mm deep. This system works extremely well for small volumes of water. However, with large amounts it tends to swill over and this can be a problem when using a central gully only, rather than one in front of each kennel.

3.   Self constructed/manufactured systems

I have seen all manner of methods used to provide adequate kennel drainage; and can vouch that most work extremely well. The two favoured methods used are half-round polyester-coated metal or ceramic tiles used to form a square channel. Both systems when correctly installed will work extremely efficiently.

As mentioned earlier, if you choose an open channel system it will be better to install twin channels; this will prevent the dilemma of trying to walk down the corridor and constantly crossing over the channel. This, combined with the effort required in trying to hold a large boisterous dog, is a recipe for an accident.

The important point to remember when installing any form of channel is to ensure that it has an adequate slope so that the water naturally runs into the drainage outlet.

3.17   KITCHEN FACILITIES

The size and fitting out of an animal kitchen can be as simple or as elaborate as you want it to be. It is highly dependent on the type of food used and the number of dogs housed.

<u>However, it should have the following basic elements:</u>

1.   Food preparation tables and sink units.
2.   Adequate hot water.
3.   Storage.
4.   Staff hand washing facility.

It may also be desirable to consider the following items, which some may consider a luxury and extravagant; however, times are changing and time spent washing-up dishes is often considered to be wasted time.

5.   Dishwasher
6.   Sluice

1.   Food preparation and sink units
In large welfare centres it has been common policy to install catering type, stainless steel kitchen equipment. It has proved to be cost effective, easy to maintain and hygienic.

Ten years ago the cost of stainless steel was prohibitive; it was a regular occurrence for me to visit industrial, hotel/catering auctions to try to purchase second-hand equipment.

However, more recently, the cost of new equipment has plummeted and is now at a level where it can purchased new for the same price as second-hand. This has the added benefit of being able to purchase the correct size and specification for the particular application.

Due to the increase use of dried dog foods, the amount of working space required has been reduced. As a general guide a kennel block of 20 dogs will have:

- 1 double bowl with double draining board - approximately 3000mm long
- 3000mm of worktop

2.   Hot water

A good supply of hot water is essential for all establishments. Apart from washing dishes and general cleaning, some welfare organisations have installed pressurised systems to enable hosepipes to be connected to the hot water system for daily washing down of the kennels and exercise runs.

The type of system used to provide the water will depend on the volume required and the mains utilities available.

The main systems available are:

2a   A centralised boiler system

This can either be gas, oil or solid fuel; on balance I would not use solid fuel due to the storage and manual handling problems. A boiler system is exactly the same, as you would have installed into a domestic home; the size may be larger to provide a greater heat output and provide the volume of hot water required. Clearly, it makes sense to combine and utilise the boiler for the kennel heating as well.

Boilers come in two systems, either:

- A conventional system - this requires the installation of a hot water storage cylinder, a cold water storage tank and a feed/expansion tank for the central heating.

- A combi system heats water directly from the cold mains, as you require it. There is no hot water storage; consequently you will require an incoming cold water main with a reliable and constant pressure to enable these units to works efficiently.

2b   Gas Multipoint heaters

For the kennel owner, who requires large amounts of hot water, these units are extremely beneficial. They will provide unlimited amounts of hot water with fast recovery rates; they can be linked to several outlets.

2c   Electric

Generally the cost for heating water electrically is more expensive than by gas or oil. It also has the disadvantage of taking longer to recover to the required temperature.

<u>The types of electric water heaters available are:</u>

Pressure type

This is probably the most suitable system for the kennel owner, it is basically a large hot water cylinder with storage capacities for 50 to 450 litres. The larger units normally have two heating elements, one in the bottom and the other at the top of the cylinder. The lower element will heat the entire contents of the cylinder and is often used on 'off-peak' electricity whilst the top is used as a boost. This system will require the installation of a cold water storage tank at high level.

Cistern type

These operate on the same principle as the pressure cylinder but they have their own built-in cold water storage tank. As the hot water is used it is replaced by the cold water from the cistern. As a rule they tend to be extremely limited in their use and capacities, normally with storage for around 25 to 135 litres.

Open type

These units are often installed over hand basins in toilets, staff rooms, etc. and are classified as 'point of use' heaters. They range in size from 6 to 136 litres and normally have a single heating element. They can be either mains supplied, or connected to a storage cistern.

Instantaneous heaters

These are designed for direct connection to the cold water mains. They operate on exactly the same principle as a domestic electric shower, i.e. a heating coil heats the water as it flows over it. These units have little benefit for the kennel owner; the water is generally only warm with poor flow rates.

Off peak electricity – If for whatever reason you decide to use electricity as your main source for heating and water heating, you should consider installing an 'off-peak' meter. This will be supplied by your electricity company and operates between 23.00hr through to 7.00am. The unit rate for this electricity is normally about a third of the daytime rate.

<table>
<tr><td colspan="2" align="center">**SIMPLIFIED SUMMARY OF HOT WATER HEATING SYSTEMS**</td></tr>
<tr><td align="center">**FIRED BOILER SYSTEMS**</td><td align="center">**ELECTRICAL**</td></tr>
<tr><td>
1. Provides large bulk storage/volume.
2. Cost effective. One boiler can serve several buildings.
3. Quick heat recovery times.
4. Professional installation required.
</td><td>
1. Ideal for isolated rooms/buildings requiring only a small amount of water.
2. Extended recovery times.
3. High revenue costs.
4. Simple installation.
</td></tr>
</table>

3.   Storage

The amount of space required in the kitchen is often overlooked, resulting in inadequate provision. Ideally all sites require some form of central bulk storage facility; this combined with storage close to the centre of activity makes life far easier. The ideal place for your daily working storage is close to the kitchen.

4.   Dishwasher

This might seem a luxury, even extravagant, but it is not as frivolous as it sounds. A large kennel with 40-60 dogs will generate around 180 dishes per day to wash; this will take a member of staff around 1-2 hours to complete. Remember this is a daily routine, which quickly becomes extremely boring and tedious.

The installation of a dishwasher will release the staff member to carry out other duties and also give far more hygienic results, due to the far higher temperatures of water used. The greater temperatures involved will destroy most bacteria/viruses and the inclusion of disinfectants will destroy any remaining.

These machines can be purchased second-hand through auctions, i.e. hotels, hospitals and catering equipment dealers. Before purchasing ensure that you have the necessary infrastructure to enable the equipment to be installed.

5.   Sluice

If your drainage system is suitable for faecal matter you will need some form of receptacle for it to be tipped or flushed into. If you do not have a suitable manhole which has a hinged or liftable lid you will need a sluice; these are either ceramic or stainless steel. The basic principle is exactly the same as a domestic toilet, although most systems use larger diameter pipework.

If you propose to install such a unit in or near the kitchen it is better, aesthetically and more hygienic to provide a dedicated room; this can also be used to store disinfectants, buckets etc. In addition you will also need to install a water supply/hosepipe to enable the utensils to be cleaned.

An alternative to the standard type of sluice is to install one of the proprietary macerator systems on the market. These consist of a sluice combined with an electric macerator pump; they normally operate from a 13amp socket and are plumbed into the drainage system.

6.   Hand basin

With the ever increasing legislation regarding Health & Safety it is becoming more important to provide suitable staff washing facilities which are separate from those used for animal related work.

3.18 DISINFECTION

Disinfection is either physical or chemical; most kennels will use chemical means, this being the most convenient. Physical methods involve the use of heat, sunlight and electricity, whilst chemical use involves liquids, gases and steam.

Whatever method you use, must be capable of destroying the virus/bacteria; it is no good using a sweet smelling compound that masks the kennel odour but does not act upon the bacteria/virus. In the main I am only going to mention chemical methods, with the exception of steam.

Chemical disinfectants act in one of three ways:

1. as oxidising agents or as reducing agents
2. as corrosives or coagulants acting upon the bacteria
3. as bacterial poisons

Most chemical disinfectants are supplied in concentrated forms and require diluting with clean water before they can be used. It is accepted that warm water not hot, is more beneficial during the mixing stage as it increases the efficiency of the disinfectant.

Once the solution has been applied it requires a 'contact time' to ensure that the bacteria/virus has been killed; this is normally between ten minutes to half an hour, after this time it can be washed/rinsed away with clean water.

Note -

1. For any disinfectant to work efficiently and correctly to destroy the bacteria, the kennel will need to be cleaned beforehand to remove faecal matter, bedding, etc.
2. Ensure that you mix the disinfectant to the correct strength as recommended by the manufacturer - too strong a mixture will not improve the efficiency of the product.
3. Do not use or mix disinfectants from different manufacturers - this can result in both compounds working against each other.
4. Ensure that all your staff know the correct dilution rates and how to mix them correctly.

Main types used:

Quaternary Ammonia Compounds

These compounds are widely used in many disinfectants e.g. Vet-Tek range, Jeyes' fluid and lysol; they are used for practically all purposes of disinfection in the kennel environment. Their action will be enhanced by the use of warm water rather than cold; they are not suitable for areas where food is being prepared.

Sodium Hypochlorite (Bleach)

This is still one of the most beneficial agents available for the kennel owner; it is one of the cheapest, it is relatively non-toxic and is generally non-irritant to the skin once it has been diluted, is readily available and breaksdown rapidly once used. All hypochlorites are unable to penetrate grease; it is for this reason that they are often used with detergents, to provide a complete cleaning system. They are particularly useful for destroying viruses.

Steam

The use of steam to clean and sterilise a kennel has many advantages; it is cost effective, extremely efficient, although this is highly dependent on the operator, and has few contra-indications. As most viruses are readily destroyed at temperatures above 70°C, the use of steam or extremely hot water will inactivate them rapidly.

Formaldehyde gas

This is mainly used to fumigate buildings. To enable this system to work efficiently the building needs to be sealed; this requires that the drains, windows, sliding hatches, etc. be adequately sealed for the duration of the process. The normal method is to provide a damp building, i.e. the walls and floor are dampened with clean water and mixing potassium permanganate with formalin generates the formaldehyde gas. Once mixed and fumigation having taken place, the building requires to be left empty for twenty-four hours. After this period the building will then require to be cleaned with clean hot water to remove all residues.

Note - The formaldehyde gas is particularly dangerous; careful attention should be given to the Health & Safety requirements of this process.

3.19 KENNEL CLEANING SYSTEMS

To clean the kennels to an effective level requires copious supplies of water and disinfectants. The level of cleanliness you require is a personal decision and is dependant on several factors i.e. type of materials used for construction, the quality of the flooring, the availability of water supply etc. We have already looked at the use of chemical methods; the practical means to enable you to carry out this process is another matter.

The general method used by larger kennels and charities is to remove faecal matter then fill buckets of warm water and the correct dilution of disinfectant. A portion of the mixture is tipped into the kennel, brushed around then left until all of the building or section has been cleaned in such a way.

The time delay from start to finish normally allows a suitable 'contact time' for the disinfectant to work. Once this process has been completed, the entire area is then washed down with clean water to remove all residues of disinfectant.

<u>In order to make this daily process as easy as possible, some thought should be given to the following:</u>

Cold water supply
Whatever system you use will require a good supply of cold water. Before embarking on a large construction programme thought should be given to ensure that the main supply is of sufficient capacity to enable the site to function all year round; this is discussed later in section four. It is also essential to check what the local Water Authority requirements are; this varies with each local authority. Generally there are two distinct systems, direct and indirect.

Direct
This system is used mainly in the Northern districts where large, high level reservoirs provide a good level of mains pressure, the main principle being that the mains incoming water supply will serve all of the sanitary fittings, cold taps and cold-water storage cistern.

As the hose supply points are fed directly off the main supply, the pressure tends to be more than adequate for the purposes of hosing and washing down the kennels. However, it is essential to establish if direct connection to the mains is legal; most water authorities will not allow this type of system where animals are concerned.

Indirect

In this system all sanitary fittings, sinks, except one drinking supply - normally the kitchen sink, are supplied from the cold-water storage cistern. It is this system that is commonly being stipulated by the water companies.

As the system feeds all the sinks and hose points, the cold-water supply cistern requires to be much larger to cope with the demands of several hose points possibly being used at the same time.

At the early stages of development it is not always possible to know the exact number of people and animals that will occupy the centre and more importantly the amount of water that will be used. All of these factors will determine what size of storage tank/s is required.

Water usage

As a general guide, the amount of water larger centres, i.e. 40 dog kennels and 30 cat units + laundry, etc. will use on a daily basis is approximately **4500 litres**.

Back siphonage

The main concern for all water companies is back siphonage or back flow into the mains supply, resulting in possible contamination. Even with double-check valves, most supply companies will not accept this as an adequate safeguard to prevent contamination where kennels are concerned.

Water supplies for buildings with inadequate mains pressure or indirect.

For high-rise buildings or buildings constructed on high ground or where an indirect system is required, it is unlikely that the mains pressure will be adequate for the purposes of providing sufficient pressure to enable the kennels to be washed down quickly and efficiently.

Remember that this is a daily process and any wasted time can quickly become a major irritation.

Direct pumping from the main

Generally, most water authorities do not allow this method to increase the water pressure to the site; this is due to the possible risks of contamination to the mains supply. The principle is that a booster pump is fitted on the incoming mains supply, thus enabling the cold-water outlets to have good pressure.

Indirect pumping from the main

This system is probably the more common one used for kennels; it being accepted by most water authorities. The basic principle is for the incoming mains supply to enter the building and run into a reservoir or cistern; this provides the 'break' between the mains supply and the outlets.

A booster pump is installed on the draw-off pipe from the cistern. It is normal practice for a low-level switch to be fitted on the cistern to protect the pump in case the water supply is used at a faster rate than which it can be supplied.

The size of the cistern and pump will depend on the amount of outlets, the size of the property, the length of, etc. Thought should be given to the number of staff who will be working in the building at the same time using hosepipes; the more staff the larger the capacities the pumps and cisterns require to be.

For smaller sites it is generally cheaper and more efficient to install booster pumps where they are required, rather than installing a centralised system. Not all your buildings will require good pressure hose outlets.

Hose pipes

It is far easier to install hose point connections around the building, rather than relying on one long length of pipe. These can be either permanently fixed or simple snap-on connections that can be moved around the building.

The shorter lengths are far less prone to wear and tear or damage.

Pressure washer

The process of cleaning by the use of hot pressure washer is an extremely effective method. These systems can be either mobile or permanently fixed; the mobile system tends to be the more common option used.

Mobile system

These units normally have a working pressure of approximately 1500psi, this being adequate for most cleaning situations. The nozzle can be changed to suit the type of work required, from a fine spray to a jet of water; your requirement should be discussed with the sales representative.

Most units are suitable for connection into a domestic 13-amp socket outlet and only require a domestic water supply. The majority hot cleaners use diesel fuel to fire the built-in boiler, which heats the water. A suitable machine will cost in the region of £2000.00 and will have a working life of around 15 years.

Helpful Hints -

▢ If you use a mobile hot pressure washer ensure that you purchase additional lengths of lance hose. This will allow the machine to be left outside while the building is being cleaned. The noise, fumes and manual handling problems associated with these large, heavy machines can be a major problem particularly with older buildings, which have narrow corridors.

Fixed system

The principle for fixed systems is exactly the same as that used on mobile systems; on the whole fixed systems tend to be larger and require three phase electrical supplies.

The advantage of this system over the mobile unit is that it is permanent, utilising fixed pipework in the building.

All that is required is for the staff to connect a short length of hose into one of the outlets provided, ensure the machine is switched on, and start to clean.

This system is particularly suited to large buildings or multi-storey complexes.

3.20   SUMMARY FOR A MODERN KENNEL

By now, you will have a good indication of what I perceive as modern, efficient kennels that not only take into account the needs of the staff but also the dogs' needs and requirements.

<u>To summarise, I believe that the guiding principles for a modern kennel are:</u>

➢ Plan ahead - It is not always cost effective to refurbish existing buildings, you may not achieve the desired result with the design and layout that is second best. Purpose-designed and constructed facilities are hard to beat. It is common for larger charities to purchase existing kennels in order to gain the existing consents, demolish the kennels and start from scratch; this is the only way to ensure a completely uniform approach.

➢ Design for the future - A green field next to you at the present might be housing estate in ten years' time.

➢ Site non-animal buildings next to potential neighbours; these will act as barriers to help screen and reduce noise levels.

➢ Have a professional land survey carried out. This is the only way to plan a large site.

➢ Small modular units - keep the numbers of dogs in any one building to a small number, i.e. a maximum of 10.

➢ Design kennels to reduce the amount of traffic in the building. Avoid long linear buildings, this type of design is a recipe for increased noise levels.

➢ Build to the highest standard you can afford - experience proves that well constructed kennels are easier to maintain, clean and offer better disease control.

➢ Well-designed kennels will be less labour intensive - this is an hidden cost that is not always apparent.

➢ Segregation of animal-related work compared with non-animal work, this will help to keep noise levels down due to fewer disturbances.

- Design the kennel to ensure that the public does not have total freedom to view all the building; the dog needs to have an inner sanctum free from disturbance; this is particularly relevant to rescue centres. This can be achieved by visitors the public only having access to the outer exercise run, leaving the central corridor as a quiet area for the dog and staff to carry out daily routines.

- Install light coloured floor/wall finishes - this immediately removes the 'prison' like appearance that has been associated with kennels and also shows up areas that might not be as clean as they could be!

- Install play equipment into large exercise runs something for the dogs to jump on, run through or climb; it all helps enhance and enrich the dogs' environment. One method is to use a fibreglass pond liner as a mould; this is filled with concrete and when dry the fibreglass liner is removed.
  Remember that it will be a considerable weight.

- Install good quality acoustic insulation to the ceilings and other high level areas - the results can be quite remarkable.

- Design floors to ensure that they drain adequately so avoiding the problem of standing water. A dry building not only presents a better image, it is safer with less chance of slipping and also reduces the risks of some viruses; a damp warm environment is a potential breeding ground for disease.

- Install solid partitions/doors where possible - these will help reduce noise breakout.

- Provide soft landscaping to the site - this will help soften the hard lines of the kennel buildings and give a far more aesthetically pleasing site.

- If you want to install a particular feature and it is not readily available, speak to a specialist company about your idea - it is surprising how willing most are to try to find a solution to your problem.

The designs I have mentioned do, I believe, represent some of the latest thinking and advances for kennels.

Everyone involved with dogs will have their own ideas on the best way to house them; there is no one single way that is correct, different methods work for different people, locations, types of dog, etc.

One thing is certain, although some of the latest kennels have come a long way and are a great improvement over kennels built ten years ago, they are still evolving and will continue to do so for many years. The improvements and modifications might only be minor, but added to some basic well-proven systems and designs things can only improve.

I do not believe in fixing something that is not broken. Moreover, I do believe that everyone can learn something new, whether it is a system, method or procedure to improve, enhance or make easier.

You should always be on the lookout for an idea that will improve your centre and raise your standards.

To sum up, I think the following four points should always be borne in mind when building new kennels:

- Plan ahead

- Think small units

- Think bright, colourful finishes

- Think Quality

4.1   MAIN UTILITY & SERVICE SUPPLIES

These hidden supplies are the lifeblood of any building whether it is kennels, a domestic house or a high rise block of flats; a modern building cannot function without them. Whatever system you have installed, needs to be effective, trouble-free and readily available.

<u>All kennels will require the following:</u>

1. A form of heating for the property.
2. Electricity to provide lighting.
3. A supply of potable cold water.

1.   Heating

As previously discussed, the type of heating you intend to use has to be decided upon early in the contract. Often the choice will be limited, usually because the utility company does not have a mains supply in your area; it is this fact that will to dictate the form of fuel you can use.

<u>The main forms of fuel are:</u>

1.a   Mains Gas.
1.b   Bulk Bottled Gas (LPG).
1.c   Oil.
1.d   Electricity.
1.e   Solid Fuel.

<u>1.a   Mains gas</u>
Clearly, this has to be the most convenient, cost-effective method for the provision of heating and hot water available. I would suggest that where possible you have a mains supply brought to your site, the problem being that for an isolated, rural centre the mains supply might be several miles away and the cost of providing a service for a single property would be prohibitive. However, it is worth checking with the supply companies see what their plans are for your particular location and obtaining a quotation for the necessary works.

1.b   Bulk bottled gas
For most rural locations without the luxury of mains supplies, this is one option available.

Once installed, the boilers only require minor adjustment to enable them to run on liquid petroleum gas (LPG). This system varies from mains supply by virtue of the fact that you will have a tank/s installed on your land; these tanks remain the property of the supplying company and you will pay a quarterly rental for each tank, approximately £15.00 per unit.

Although this system works extremely efficiently, on the whole the gas is more expensive than mains supplied and at the present time more expensive than oil. The size of tanks required will depend on the usage, the size of the boilers and the number of boilers on the site.

An average tank capable of running a large boiler will measure 2m x 1m, the driver will need reasonable access to fill it and it must be sited at least 3m off your boundary and at least 6m away from a residential building.

1.c   Oil
As with gas you will need to install a suitable tank; the minimum capacity should be 1000 litres. The larger tanks are suitable for large commercial boilers with high outputs (BTU), a central storage system serving several boilers, or a site with potential access problems, particularly during the winter months.

Unlike gas, which is distributed under pressure, most oil systems work on gravity, i.e. the tank has to be at the same height as the boiler; this might entail the tank being raised on blocks.

Oil comes in two grades for domestic use - 28 second (kerosene) and 35 second (gas oil). When ordering oil or replacement/additional boilers, this must be borne in mind and compatible units installed.

A boiler designed to run on one grade and set up as such will not run on any other grade without some modification to the burner. Kerosene is the cleaner of the two fuels and therefore is slightly more expensive.

1.d   Electricity

A site can be powered entirely by electricity; it will be relatively cheap to install, but the running costs will be extremely high. It has several other disadvantages; it is not as flexible as gas or oil when dealing with large volumes of hot water; it is extremely limited when looking at large commercial laundry equipment and you will be hard pressed to find second-hand, electrically operated machines.

For an all electric site the incoming cable will probably be a three-phase supply; usually on a commercial tariff and billed monthly.
On the whole, I would not recommend a large site being powered entirely by electricity.

1.e   Solid fuel

This is another possibility in terms of supplying power/heat to the site. It is not an option that has much merit; apart form the storage fuels, the considerable time and effort required to top-up the boiler, even with a modern hopper feed system is a major consideration. It involves considerable manual handling; compared with the alternatives available it has little to offer a large, busy kennel complex, which would not generally have the dedicated staff to look after such systems.

2.   Electricity

As has already been stated, to run a site entirely by electricity is expensive, does not have the flexibility of many of the other systems available and is more likely to be affected by adverse weather or interruptions to the supply.

3.   Water supply

All premises require a good supply of potable water. Generally this is supplied by one of the water utility companies; however the water could come from a private supply or a bore well.

Whichever system you have must be capable of supplying all your requirements, <u>all year round</u>. It is pointless having a private supply that is incapable of providing water all year, the problems with private supplies are generally more pronounced during the summer months.

As previously mentioned a centre with 40 kennels and 30 cat units + laundry will use approximately **4500 litres** per day.

<u>A typical mains supply coming from one of the water companies will be in three parts:</u>

1. Water company service main.

2. A service pipe, which is still the property of the Water Company. The pipe runs from the service main to the boundary of your property, where it is terminated by a stopcock.

   The size of the incoming service pipe will be determined by the amount of water that will be used; for a larger site either a 32mm or a 50mm service pipe would be suitable; the larger the pipe the higher the standing charge will be.

3. The supply pipe from the stopcock into the property is the responsibility of the consumer.

Water Metering
Within the next few years all commercial companies will have water meters; some areas have already started a compulsory programme of installing them.

Meters, where fitted, are read on a quarterly basis by the water company; the water used is charged per each cubic metre as measured by the meter.

4.2 FIRE PROTECTION

The specific laws relating to fire safety will be dealt with later on in section 5. Kennel buildings by their very nature do not on the whole represent a significant fire risk; the solid nature of construction and the lack of inflammable materials all help to reduce the risk.

In addition, where a relatively small number of staff is employed, i.e. less than 20, a Fire Certificate will not be required.

The normal procedure when applying for Building Regulations Approval is for the officer concerned to pass a set of the plans to the Fire Brigade. The plans will be assessed and recommendations made for any specific requirements; for most small kennels the minimum recommendation would possibly be for portable fire extinguishers or fire doors with overhead closing devices.

Insurance companies may also stipulate the level of equipment required for a particular location and operation.

The basic elements for domestic and small commercial operations can be divided into three elements:

1. Fire detection and alarms systems.
2. Emergency lighting.
3. Portable fire fighting equipment.

1.   Fire Detection and Alarms

There is a vast range of systems available on the market from simple battery operated; stand-alone units to fully integrated systems linked to intruder alarms. The level with which your insurance company and the fire authority are satisfied will depend on the layout of the centre, the size of the building, the number of staff employed and any high-risk operations that might be carried out. However, most animal welfare establishments and kennels are classed as low risk properties and therefore do not normally require a sophisticated system.

The purpose of fire detection and alarm systems is to act as an early warning system. The more time there is to initiate the appropriate action, the less likelihood of serious damage or loss of life. Fire detection should not be viewed as an unnecessary expense, a waste of time or something that may never be used; the sooner a fire is detected, the more chance of initiating the appropriate action and limiting the damage.

The cost of installing a basic system is an extremely small percentage of the overall project cost.

The minimum requirement is a battery operated stand-alone unit, which will give an audible alarm in the region of 90dB. Clearly this type of unit has its limitations and this must be taken into account when looking at the site layout, distance of the kennels from any residential, etc. A more permanent solution is to install a basic system of heat/smoke detectors linked to a control panel with manual call points and an external audible alarm. The advantage with these systems is that the buildings can be 'zoned' if required. This would enable a staff member chance to go directly to the fire zone without having to spend time looking for the fire.

2.   Emergency Lighting

The aim of emergency lighting is to indicate the emergency escape routes, to show changes of direction, to show where the fire alarm call points and fire extinguishers are located and also to enable emergency work to be carried out or completed.

The types of lighting available are:

a.   Some luminaries with emergency battery back-up.
b.   Wall mounted plug in, battery operated units.
c.   A central battery system, which powers all of the luminaries.
d.   A back-up generator capable of providing power to all the lights. This has the added benefit of being able to provide power to enable the rest of the site to continue to function.

Due to the relatively simple construction and layout of most single storey kennels, the normal requirement is for a very basic system, which covers the legal requirements and also enables basic duties to continue during a power cut.

Whichever system is installed it must be maintained and capable of working when it is required to do so.

3. Portable Fire Fighting Equipment

The installation of portable fire extinguishers is a legal and usually an insurance requirement. Most kennels will only have this type of equipment installed; the installation of fixed, centralised, monitored systems will not be required for most single storey kennels.

The type and number of extinguishers required is dependent upon the size of the premises and the risks of fire involved; advice should be sought from insurance companies, extinguisher suppliers, the fire officer or from the British Standard 5306, Part 3.

When talking about fire extinguishers we are dealing only with small isolated fires that can be extinguished quickly and safely; we are not concerned with large fires that have engulfed an entire room or a more extensive area.

Once a fire has reached this latter stage the only safe action is to vacate the building and call the Fire Brigade.

Types of extinguisher

Until recently all extinguishers were colour coded. However, under new EU legislation all new extinguishers are the same colour but have a small coloured band showing the type of fire for which it is suitable. Eventually all older types will be phased out. It is important to know the type of fire extinguishers and the types of fire on which it can safely be used.

The basic types are:

Water (RED) - Used for cooling organic materials, i.e. paper, wood, textiles, etc.
Foam (CREAM) - Used for flammable liquids such as petrol, oil and fats
Powder (BLUE) - As for foam but can also be used on electrical fires
Carbon dioxide (BLACK) - As for foam but safe to use on electrical fires

The other systems available are:

Hose reels

Recommended particularly for floor areas in excess of 800m^2. Extremely effective on certain classes of fire, they deliver an unlimited supply of water and with sufficient mains pressure can deliver a jet of water in excess of 6m. A standard hose is normally 30m in length and has an internal diameter of 19mm.

Fire blanket
This is used to smother small fires involving liquids and organic materials.

All of the above appliances need to be sited in the most suitable place, generally:

1. As close as possible to any fire risk.
2. Close/adjacent to doorways.
3. On escape routes.
4. At the same location in identical buildings.
5. Near "fire points".
6. Away from extremes of temperature.

The extinguishers need to be securely fixed to walls, approximately 900mm above the floor. This will prevent the base from rusting, particularly in kennel environments, and also prevent them being used as 'door stops'!

They should be visible at all times and staff should be aware of their location and, more importantly, how to use them.

It is pointless having extinguishers on the premises if none of the staff can operate them. Most supplying companies will offer an annual inspection to ensure that the units are fully charged and capable of working; this can also be an ideal time to train staff to operate an extinguisher.

It is surprising how difficult some people find the procedure of discharging an extinguisher; any form of practice might make the difference between a minor fire and a major disaster!

4.3   SITE DRAINAGE/SEWAGE DISPOSAL SYSTEMS

The legal requirements for the discharge of sewage are covered under the Building Regulations and the Environmental Protection Act 1995.

The safe and efficient disposal of foul and surface water is taken as a 'right' in this country and should be considered as of being of major importance to the health and welfare of staff/visitors and animals on the site.

Any poorly constructed system will not only affect your site; but could have far reaching consequences with pollution to water supplies/courses and contamination to others' land, resulting in prosecution.

A kennel owner has several choices available for the proper disposal of foul/waste and surface water.

The main systems are:

1. Sewer (public and private).
2. Pumped sewage system.
3. Cesspool.
4. Septic or settlement tank.
5. Biological filter or treatment plant.
6. Filtration mound.
7. Reed bed.

1. Sewer

A sewer can either be a private or public one. Most sewers built on private land since 1937 are private, but not all. The local authority should be able to give advice and guidance on this, as they are required to keep detailed maps. A private sewer is the responsibility of the owners of the buildings that it serves and all costs are shared unless there has been a legal agreement drawn up or it is documented in the deeds to the contrary.

Public sewers are generally sewers constructed before 1937, can be of any size and can run across private land, although most run under the public road system.
All public sewers are maintained by the local authority, which acts as agents for the water authority. The local authority will normally insist that any site or property within 30m of a public sewer has its foul water drainage system connected to that sewer.

145

However, the problems experienced by sites located in rural areas and not served by a municipal sewage system can be a major source of worry, expense and difficulty to the property owner. At all costs it is recommended that you endeavour to connect into the main sewerage system; in the long-term it is far cheaper, with less problems likely to occur and is generally a far cleaner solution.

In fact, the Environment Agency prefers and has encouraged certain trade and commercial operations to discharge into sewers rather than watercourses, the reasoning being that the municipal treatment plants are more sophisticated and far more able to monitor and balance the overall quality of the effluent.

Sewerage undertakers control all trade waste disposed of into a sewer and are normally a subsidiary of the water companies.

<u>Any form of trade discharge has to have the consent of the sewerage undertaker, who has the right to control:</u>

- The nature of the effluent.
- The maximum daily volume allowed.
- The maximum rate of flow.
- The sewer into which the effluent is discharged.

Experience shows that there should not be any difficulties in obtaining permission to discharge into a main sewer. On the whole the amount and type of discharge produced by even the largest kennels is still relatively small and non-toxic, being primarily clean wash-down, and is of little concern to the sewage companies.

2. Pumped sewage system

Ideally, all drainage systems should work by gravity, with the effluent running into the sewer. Often, particularly in rural areas a public sewer might be available, but some distance away or at a higher level than your site, necessitating the need to pump the effluent under pressure, uphill through small bore pipes.

For most situations the installation of a packaged pumping station is the most cost effective. These come in a range of sizes, grades of pump and are highly suitable for most kennel applications. The pumps are generally submersible, electrically operated and require little maintenance.

Helpful Hints -

📖 Make a full investigation of suppliers of package systems; these can vary tremendously in price.

📖 Explain fully what the pumps will have to cope with, i.e. the type/amount of solid material, etc.

📖 Most package systems require a three-phase electricity supply; single-phase pumps are available but are not as robust and capable of dealing with the larger solids. The use of an electrical converter will allow the use of a three-phase pump on a single-phase electricity supply. This is a cost-effective solution for a site that does not have a three-phase supply.

📖 Install hair/grease traps to prevent dog hairs, etc. from entering/blocking up the pumps.

📖 Try to site the package system close to an access point as it will require to be cleaned out periodically

3. Cesspool

A cesspool is an underground, watertight storage reservoir used for domestic purposes, but sized correctly can be used for commercial operations. The size of the tank should be a minimum of 18000 litres, but not more than 45000 litres.

However, before installing such a tank, carefully establish the volume of liquids entering it and the costs pumping it out.

As already mentioned, an average, medium sized centre will use on average approximately 4000 to 5000 litres per day, seven days a week. With a cost of approximately £150.00 to £200.00 for every 5000 litres to pump out and remove, this quickly becomes an expensive method of disposal.

Building Regulations state that cesspools should be sited at least 15m away from a dwelling and 18m away from any spring, well or stream used for drinking water.

The use of cesspools is restricted to areas that do not have mains drainage and where the subsoil conditions do not allow the use of septic tanks. The main reasons for this being: lack of permeability, such as clay or dense rock, or being close to areas containing springs, wells and other drinking water supplies.

A modern cesspool is usually constructed out of glass reinforced plastic, although brick, concrete and even steel systems are used. Cesspools need to be emptied frequently, usually every 4-6 weeks.

Helpful Hints -

📖 Ensure that there is good access for the tanker, this requires to be within approximately 25m of the tank and should also take into account the depth of the tank.

📖 Ensure that no storm water enters the system as this would quickly overload the tank and is expensive to have taken away.

4. Septic or settlement tank

If mains sewerage systems are not available and for financial reasons it is not viable to install a cesspool, then several options remain, the cheapest and simplest being a septic tank or settlement tank (as it is referred to in some areas).

These tanks differ from cesspools by having an outlet, which allows the effluent to soakaway naturally by the use of surface, subsoil drainage pipes or to flow directly into a stream or river.

For obvious reasons the use of surface irrigation is not ideal as it sterilises available land and more importantly, can be a health hazard. The cleaner and preferred method is to lay a series of underground pipes, which are either open-jointed, porous or perforated and can be laid to either a herringbone or grid system.

<u>All direct discharges from a septic tank whether into a subsoil system, stream or river requires the consent of the Environmental Agency. This will be discussed at the end of this section.</u>

 For a septic tank to function, particularly where a large volume of effluent is produced requires suitable porous subsoil such as sand, gravel or chalk. The extent of subsoil drainage system will depend on the porosity of the land and therefore, before installing such a system a site investigation or porosity test should be carried out.

A ground engineer or reputable builder will be able to carry out this investigation work for you. Ideally this should be a person who knows the local ground conditions.

One consideration to be borne in mind if installing a septic tank is how to provide adequate soakaway for the final discharge.

For larger centres or ground conditions that have poor porosity the total length of the underground pipe system could be over 50m in length.

A septic tank system should be airtight to ensure that anaerobic action takes place. Such a tank does not purify the effluent but merely breaks down the solids by the means of anaerobic bacteria, and decomposes the organic matter into methane and carbon dioxide.

The heavy sludge than falls to the bottom of the tank whilst the scum floats and settles on the top. A well-balanced tank will have a thick layer of scum on its surface; this will help exclude air and ensure that the system operates to its full efficiency.

One problem with using septic tanks for kennels is the 'loading' factor. Most kennels wash and clean in a relatively short period but if the wash-down water is allowed to run directly into the tank it could overload it. In order to prevent this, a common practice is to install an in-line holding-tank above the septic tank, which will allow the load to be balanced over a longer period of time.

Septic tanks come in a range of construction materials and most older systems used for domestic properties are constructed from brick or concrete. Most modern tanks are constructed out of glass reinforced plastic (GRP).

All systems work on the same design principle to a lesser or greater degree.

<u>The operation of a modern GRP system is:</u>

1. Sewage enters the main chamber of the tank; this is the sludge holding and decomposition section.

2. From the sludge holding chamber, the effluent rises into smaller chambers where sedimentation of finer solids occurs thus allowing large sediment to return to the lower chamber.

3. From this final chamber the clarified effluent is discharged into the sub-soil drainage system, stream/river or has further treatment.

4. The solids will need to be removed by suction tanker. This is carried out approximately every 6 to12 months. A small portion of the solids is left in the bottom of the tank to enable the active bacteria to multiply.

5. Biological filter or treatment plant

Biological filters are normally installed where the Environmental Agency requires higher discharge consents. Most modern biofilters are complete packaged systems, normally manufactured from GRP or polyethylene.

<u>The systems I have seen used for kennels are:</u>

Activated sludge

These systems work on the principle of continuously moving or agitating the effluent, either by air or mechanical means. Effluent enters a primary settlement tank where settlement of the solids takes place, from where the displaced supernatant liquor enters the main activation tank.

During this aeration stage the bacteria or activated sludge multiplies to remove most of the organic pollutants. After the agitation period the effluent is allowed to settle for a further period, the activated sludge settles at the bottom of the tank and the clarified water being discharged into the drainage system.

Trickling filters

After the effluent has entered and settled in the primary tank, the supernatant liquor enters the main filter unit. The filtration unit makes use of irregular shaped pieces of plastic over which the effluent is allowed to trickle via a rotating system or a shaped disc with holes. Biological treatment takes place in the filter tank by the process of bacteriological oxidation and the oxidising bacteria collect on the plastic media, and form a jelly-like substance called 'biomass'.

A stage of final settlement is allowed to take place before the effluent is discharged in the watercourse or sub-soil drainage system. The method and means of air entering the system will depend on the manufacturer's specification, with some systems air is forced through the top whilst with others air is blown in from the bottom of the filtration tank.

Rotating biological filters (RBCs)

These filters operate on a system of rotating discs housed within a packaged unit. They rely upon a colony of micro-organisms becoming established between the discs, which rotate partly submerged through the wastewater. The colony is exposed to the air and to the organic material of the effluent.

The system to be installed will have to take into consideration the consent granted for the level of discharge, the volume of effluent and the number of people/animals on your site. The installation might be a combination of two systems e.g. trickling filter and an activated sludge.

Where current systems are already in place but are not performing to the required discharge consent, then there is a need to install a secondary or tertiary system.

The two main systems are:

6. Filtration mound

A filtration mound is an extremely efficient way of polishing the final effluent. It is basically a large biological treatment plant and the size and extent of the pipework system will depend on the final level of treatment required to satisfy the Environmental Agency.

The mound is normally installed below ground, with a network of perforated pipes being allowed to discharge the treated effluent, usually on a timed and batched process, through a series of layered sands and aggregates. A cut-off drain is installed and all of the polished effluent runs into this and is finally discharged into the watercourse or sub-soil drainage system.

This system has given excellent results e.g. one installation reduced the ammonia from around 15mg/L to 3mg/L. Minimal maintenance is required and the ground above it can be used for lightweight operations e.g. to exercise dogs.

7. Reed bed

The use of reed beds is becoming increasingly popular as a method of providing secondary treatment with the benefits of low maintenance, an aesthetic appearance, are economic and provide extremely high levels of purification.

Like filtration mounds they require additional land, the size being dictated by the volume of effluent, numbers of people/animals and the consent standard granted.

The system works by the reeds' ability to pass oxygen, absorbed by the leaf system, down to their roots. The polluted water passes around the roots and becomes purified by the high concentrations of micro-organisms living there.

Helpful Hints -

⚏ Ensure that all of the relevant information is given to the prospective suppliers, i.e. volume of water used, type and quantity of disinfectant, number of staff/animals on site.

⚏ Check to see if the system is capable of dealing with dog faeces; some systems are not suitable.

⚏ Plan ahead – Take into account possible future expansion of the premises and an increase in the number of staff and animals. Perhaps it will be more cost effective to look at a slightly larger plant.

⚏ What laundry arrangements have been made? A large commercial machine will use a significant volume of water and detergents.

⚏ Disinfectants. All biofilters are highly sensitive to disinfectants, soaps, etc. and the micro-organisms can easily be destroyed by the use of too much disinfectant. The wrong type of disinfectant can also be detrimental.

⚏ Allow for possible extensions or secondary treatment to your existing system. The legislation regarding waste is constantly changing and is generally becoming more restrictive. Plan accordingly and allow for obtaining consent for a higher level of discharge is a few years' time.

⚏ Monitor the site and be flexible, if there has been a busy period with more visitors than normal then the current sludge emptying cycle might not be sufficient and might need to be increased.

What to do if the system fails to achieve its discharge consent.

The points given below show suggested actions to be taken should the filtration system fail to achieve the standard required for the appropriate consent.

- Contact the suppliers/manufacturers for advice.

- Ensure that the plant is regularly serviced.

- Check to see if the circulation fans are working. Most modern systems have some method to force air into the system.

- Has the plant been regularly desludged? Is the frequency sufficient to ensure that the holding tank is not overflowing into the secondary chamber?

- Has there been an overdose of chemicals; most treatment plants will take three/four weeks to re-establish themselves?

- Do you need to balance the hydraulic loading?

- Does the plant need the inclusion of additives to help the micro-organisms build up to a sufficient level?

- Most plants will have a reduction in efficiency during the winter particularly if a severe, and/or prolonged one. At any temperature below 10°C, the metabolism of the bacteria will decrease rapidly.

- Is the filter media becoming waterlogged or clogged? If so, this will require flushing through with fresh water.

- Has the site grown to the extent that the plant is not capable of reaching the original consent standard?

Once the system has been installed remember that like all mechanical items it needs to be maintained and monitored.

It is worth regularly having samples of effluent analysed by an accredited company/laboratory to establish if the system is working correctly. This also ensures that there is time to correct any problems found before they become major and the Environmental Agency becomes involved.

A copy of the analysis should be sent to the Environmental Agency, even if the system has failed. This proactive approach will demonstrate your commitment to correcting the problem and in the worst case, could prevent you from being prosecuted by the Environmental Agency.

DISCHARGE CONSENTS

All consents for commercial discharges are the responsibility of the Environmental Agency; they will set the standard for your particular plant. This standard is an individual one for each particular site and takes into account location, type of discharge point, i.e. stream/river or subsoil drainage, the volume of effluent and the nature of the business.

Once consent has been granted, the system will have to comply with the set limits. It is normal for the EA to monitor effluent on a regular basis; this is usually 2-4 times per year. If the plant fails to reach the set standard the problem must not be ignored; it will not resolve itself and must be corrected.

If the system has failed then remedial action must be taken as suggested above.

4.4   FAECES DISPOSAL

The legal definition for clinical waste is given in section 2.11.

The categories fall into five groups for the varying levels of contamination, these groups are as follows:

A   **1** - soiled surgical dressings, swabs and all other contaminated waste from treatment areas.
2 - waste materials, where the Control of Substances Hazardous to Health Regulations (COSHH) assessment indicates a risk to staff handling them, for example from infectious disease cases.
3 - all human tissue, including blood (whether infected or not), animal carcasses and tissues from veterinary centres, hospitals or laboratories and all related swabs and dressings.

B   discarded syringe needles, cartridges, broken glass and other contaminated disposable sharp instruments or items.

C   microbiological cultures and potentially infected waste from pathology departments, clinical or research departments.

D   certain pharmaceutical and chemical waste.

E   used disposable bedpan liners, urine containers and incontinence pads.

Disposal of animal faeces might seem a simple problem to overcome, but from experience it can be expensive, time consuming and very difficult to resolve.

The options available are:

1. Main sewer.
2. Biological treatment plant/septic tank.
3. Landfill.
4. Incineration.
5. Composting.

1. Main sewer

This is perhaps the preferred option, being the most convenient, most hygienic and probably causing the least environmental damage. Most authorities categorise faecal matter under group E, which is suitable for disposal to sewers, particularly for small amounts.

As already discussed, any discharges to the sewer require the approval of the Sewerage Authority; they will set the limits and conditions for the discharge. Due to the relatively small amounts involved these conditions are generally not too onerous.

2. Biological plant or septic tank

The method of disposal of faecal matter into your treatment plant will depend on several factors; i.e. can the plant handle the type of organic load? What is the final discharge point?

Will the Environmental Agency allow faecal matter to be disposed of in your area to a watercourse or subsoil drainage system? If so this option is very similar to disposal via the main sewer, being convenient, hygienic and cost effective.

3. Landfill

This option normally requires the services of a registered waste carrier. However before entering into an expensive contract with a waste carrier, check with the local authority to establish the policy in force for the collection of animal waste.

As already stated, this can vary from one authority to another and will take into account the location and amount of waste that is likely to be produced from the site.

If landfill, whether by the local authority or specialist carrier is the simplest or preferred option, then consider the segregation of clinical waste from normal trade waste; as clinical waste is prohibitively more expensive to dispose of than normal waste.

The following scheme has generally been adopted:

BAG COLOUR	TYPE OF WASTE
BLACK	Normal domestic "household waste" not to be treated as clinical waste
YELLOW	All waste destined for incineration. These will be clearly marked "for incineration only"
YELLOW WITH BLACK STRIPES	Waste which should preferably be disposed of by incineration but may be disposed of by landfill
LIGHT BLUE	Waste for autoclaving (or equivalent treatment) before ultimate disposal
RED OR WHITE WITH RED STRIPE	Soiled linen

4.   Incineration

This is generally the most expensive option available to the kennel owner and will depend on the suitability of an incineration plant being within a suitable distance of the property. Obviously the further distances involved, the greater the costs.

With this option the standard method of using plastic bags is totally unsuitable for most faecal matter, yellow plastic bins with sealable lids will need to be supplied by the carrier/ incineration company. These are collected in the same way as plastic bags but are far more hygienic.

The bins are usually available in two sizes, i.e. 20 or 35 litre.

5. Composting

Composting has been around for a long while and is used extensively in Scandinavia for the disposal of domestic waste from isolated properties and communities. All animal waste will decompose naturally if left in the open air, but the process is slow.

The other main obstacle to be overcome is the physical element of handling faecal matter.

As a country where traditionally we have little interest where all of our waste goes to once it has left our property, it is difficult to come to terms with the prospect of looking at alternative systems that are just not as convenient.

Decomposition of animal waste requires it to be mixed with some form of carbonaceous material such as straw, chipbark or newspaper to provide voids through which air can be blown. The amount of air is adjusted to provide the desired temperature for the waste.

The optimum temperature is around 55°C for decomposition and the control of pathogenic bacteria; the end product is suitable for use as a fertiliser on the land.

4.5   LANDSCAPING - (Trees near buildings)

Most planning applications will require some form of landscaping to the site; the extent required will vary according to the site, its location and the size of the development.

There is no question that a professionally landscaped site will improve the general appearance of that site beyond all recognition, will soften the overall appearance, can help with noise reduction, particularly by screening off private areas and non-animal work, and will enhance the property for your visitors/public.

If you propose to, or are required to carry out landscaping operations, it is worthwhile looking at the British Standard books on this subject, or discussing it with a qualified landscape contractor or architect. Advice will be needed on the types of tree suitable for your location and how far they should be planted away from the buildings; this is particularly important.

Remember a mature oak or elm tree can grow to over 20m in height and imagine their effect on the buildings and foundations in twenty years' time.

Landscaping on a site should ideally be planned as part of the main construction, to allow for the most suitable species in relation to buildings, underground drainage pipes, service mains, etc. It should also take into account the proximity of neighbours' services, buildings, etc.

A registered landscape contractor will advise on and design a suitable scheme for a site as part of his contract. It is also common practice for them to advise on any necessary replacements for trees/shrubs that have died and to provide a maintenance programme for the first year following completion of the contract.

5.0 HEALTH AND SAFETY

All businesses are compelled to comply with certain legal obligations and regulations irrespective to the size of the business; these regulations apply to both the employee and the employer.

Like all legislation the rules are complex and constantly changing; therefore only an overview is given of the relevant legislation to ensure that the employer is aware of the effect of the main legislation.

Full guides to the legislation can be obtained from HMSO Publications and specialised publications such as Croner's.

5.1 HEALTH AND SAFETY AT WORK ACT 1974

The broad aims of the Health and Safety at Work Act 1974 are essentially:

- To secure the health, safety and welfare of persons at work.
- To protect persons other than employees from risks at work (e.g. persons living or working near the business or these entering the premises in the course of business).
- To control dangerous substances in terms of acquisition or use.
- To control emissions into the atmosphere from the workplace.

Failure to comply with the Act or any regulations made under it is a criminal offence and the employer, or even the employee may be prosecuted.

Health and Safety Policy Statement

At present any employer who has five or more employees must prepare a written statement of their general policy on Health and Safety. This policy will not be cast in stone; it will evolve to take into account changes in management, legal requirements and technological changes.

As a policy is unique to a particular property and the hazards associated with it, there can be no single standard form. However, the policy content is normally covered in three parts for most small businesses -

1. The company's general declaration on health, safety and welfare.
2. The internal organisation and administration of the policy.
3. The detailed safety rules, arrangements and codes of practice relating. Specifically to the hazards and risks associated with the business and the works carried out.

GUIDANCE NOTES -

1.   The general declaration should include a commitment by the company to adhere to the provisions of the 1974 Act and all relevant legislation in order to promote and maintain all standards of health and safety for the employees whilst at work

2.   The internal organisation and administration section of the policy should clearly show the defined areas and limits of responsibilities

3.   The third section should highlight all the hazards or risks that might be associated with the work carried out. For kennels these will include handling of difficult dogs; problems likely to be associated with disinfectants; manual handling, noise, etc. The company's policy on Fire Safety should also be addressed; this should include suitable training, evacuation procedures, responsibility for calling assistance, etc.

Duties of Employees - Sections 7 and 8 of the Health and Safety at Work Act 1974 require every employee to have the following responsibilities:

to take reasonable care for the health and safety of himself and other persons who may be affected by his acts or omissions at work and as regards who any duty or requirement imposed on his employer or any other persons to co-operate with him so far as is necessary to enable that duty or requirement to be performed or complied with.

Also-
No person shall intentionally or recklessly interfere with or misuse anything provided in the interests of health, safety or welfare in pursuance of any of the relevant statutory provisions.

5.2   ACCIDENTS AT WORK

The legislation regarding accidents at work in commercial premises is contained in the **Reporting of Injuries, Diseases and Dangerous Occurrences Regulations 1995 (RIDDOR).** The aim of these regulations is to ensure that accidents, which occur in the workplace, are investigated and, where possible, remedial measures are taken to avoid recurrence.

An accident is normally defined as one of the following and is reported to the Health and Safety Executive (HSE):

a.   Fatal accidents.
b.   Major accidents/conditions.
c.   Incidents where as a result of an accident connected with the workplace, people not at work are injured and have to be taken to hospital for treatment.
d.   An incident where a person not at work suffers a major injury as a result of work being carried out and has to be treated at a hospital.
e.   Dangerous occurrences.
f.   Accidents which cause more than three days' incapacity off work.
g.   Certain work-related diseases.

An accident includes any non-consensual act of physical violence suffered at work.

Major accidents/conditions are as follows:

a.   Any fracture (except fingers, thumbs or toes).
b.   Any amputation.
c.   Dislocation of the shoulder, hip, knee or spine.
d.   Loss of sight (either temporarily or permanent).
e.   Chemical or hot metal burn to the eye or any penetrating liquid to the eye.
f.   Any injury resulting from electrical shock or electrical burn leading to unconsciousness or requiring resuscitation or admittance to hospital for more than 24 hours.
g.   Any other injury which leads to: hypothermia, heat-induced illness, unconsciousness, or requires admittance to hospital for more than 24 hours.
h.   Loss of consciousness caused by asphyxia or by exposure to a harmful substance by any other route.
i.   Acute illness requiring medical treatment or loss of consciousness caused by substances by any other route.
j.   Acute illness, which is believed to result from exposure to a biological agent, its toxins or from infected material.

Absence

When calculating the three days of absence, this does not include the day of the accident. Any normal non-working days, i.e. weekends, are included and incapacity for work means that the person is incapacitated from normal work, rather than being physically absent from work

Reporting of accidents

The employer is the person responsible for reporting death, major injury, incapacity for work or disease suffered by an employee.

In all other cases the responsibility rests with the person in control of the premises connected with the undertaking.

The report is normally to the HSE and takes the following format:

a. Death - a written report of an employee who dies within one year as the result of a reportable injury and any other who dies as a result of a work-related accident.

b. Major injury or dangerous occurrence - notification by the quickest practicable means followed by a written report within 10 days of the event; the report should be on a Form 2508.

c. Incapacity for work - a report to be sent as soon as practicable and within 10 days of the accident; the report should be made on a Form 2508.

d. Specified disease - a report on a Form 2508A to be sent immediately after receipt of a written statement from a medical practitioner.

5.3 PERSONAL PROTECTIVE EQUIPMENT AT WORK REGULATIONS 1992

Personal Protective Equipment (PPE) means all equipment (including clothing affording protection against the weather) which is intended to be worn or held by a person at work and which protects him/her against one or more risks to his/her health, safety and welfare.

PPE includes such items as aprons, gloves, safety footwear, eye protection, ear defenders, respirators, etc.

PPE is, as it states, personal protective equipment for an individual; it is not for communal use; the person given the equipment should have suitable provision to secure his/her equipment away after use.

PPE is normally the "last resort" and only to be provided where engineering controls and safe systems at work do not effectively control the risks identified.

The problems associated with PPE are:

a. PPE only protects the person wearing it.
b. Maximum levels of protection with PPE are seldom achieved; in practice the actual level of protection is difficult to assess.
c. PPE may restrict the wearer's movements, visibility, hearing and provide additional weight to be carried.

5.4 DISABILITY DISCRIMINATION ACT 1995

The Disability Discrimination Act 1995 requires that employers and service providers treat disabled people no less favourably than someone who is able bodied.

Description of Disability *- The Act defines disability as a physical or mental impairment, which has a substantial and long-term adverse effect on a person's ability to carry out normal day-to-day activities.*

People who have a disability, and people who have had a disability but no longer have one, are covered by the Act.

Building Regulations

A building or extension to a building comprising an employer's premises may have been constructed in accordance with Part M of the building regulations, which covers access and facilities for the disabled.

Employers do not have to alter any physical characteristics of their premises, which still satisfy the building regulations in force when the premises were built, but changes to the premises may be required to characteristics not covered by the regulations.

Sample of reasonable adjustments - making changes.

Employers may have to make one or several of the following changes:

- Alteration of premises.
- Allocation of some duties to another employee.
- Transfer of a person to fill an existing vacancy.
- Alteration of working hours.
- Allowance of additional time off for rehabilitation, training or assessment.
- Additional allowances for time allocated to carry out a procedure.

These are just a small selection of some of the improvements/alterations that an employer may have to make.

5.5   ENVIRONMENTAL PROTECTION ACT 1990

The **Environmental Protection Act 1990** (Part III) draws together most of the statutory nuisances from earlier legislation and amends some of the definitions and rationalises them.

Under the 1990 Act, there is a duty for every local authority to "cause its area to be inspected from time to time to detect any statutory nuisances which ought to be dealt with".

<u>The list of proposed statutory nuisances as in Part III of the 1990 Act is as follows:</u>

1.   Any premises maintained in such a state as to be prejudicial to health or a nuisance.
2.   Smoke emitted from premises so as to be prejudicial to health or a nuisance. This does not apply to:
      a. Smoke emitted from a chimney of a building in a smoke controlled area
      b. Dark smoke emitted from a chimney of a building, or chimney serving the furnace of a boiler or industrial plant attached to a building or for the time being fixed to or installed on any land.
      c. Smoke emitted from a railway engine.
      d. Dark smoke emitted otherwise than as mentioned above from industrial or trade premises.
3.   Fumes or gases emitted from premises (private dwellings) so as to be prejudicial to health or a nuisance.
4.   Any dust, steam, smell or other effluvia arising on industrial, trade or business premises and being prejudicial to health or a nuisance.
5.   Any accumulation of deposit which is prejudicial to health or a nuisance
6.   Any animal kept in such a place or manner as to be prejudicial to health or nuisance.
7.   Noise emitted from premises so as to be prejudicial to health or a nuisance.
8.   Any other matter declared by any enactment to be a statutory nuisance.

Available defences –

Clearly the kennel owner will need to take careful note of sections 4,5,6 and 7, these being the areas where most owners encounter problems with local authorities.

Some defences against action for nuisances are:

1. Act of God.

2. Act of a trespasser.

3. Action taken without the owner's consent.

4. Owner ignorant of causing a nuisance.

5. Statutory authority - this refers to the situation where doing something otherwise unlawful is authorised by statute. The statute takes away any right of action in respect of the nuisance complained about. This indemnity extends not only to the act itself but also to any related consequences.

6. Best Practicable Means (BPM) - If BPM had been used in an attempt to prevent the nuisance occurring then that is an acceptable defence for any industry, trade or business. Section 79 of the Environmental Protection Act 1990 defines the concept of BPM as taking into account local conditions, current technical knowledge and financial implications. BPM can cover design, installation, maintenance and periods of operation of plant and the design, construction and maintenance of buildings and enclosures.

The availability of the above defences depends on the details of the individual case.

DUTY OF CARE

Under Section 34 of the Environmental Protection Act 1990 all producers of waste are compelled to dispose of it in such a manner as not to endanger public health or the environment; this is known as "duty of care".

All waste produced on the site has to be transported by a registered carrier and disposed of at an authorised facility.

Under **The Environmental Protection (Duty of Care) Regulations 1991** a mandatory system of transfer notes was introduced.

A transfer note is completed for each collection of waste and is signed by the transferor and transferee.

The note will contain the following information:

- Identification of waste.
- Quantity of waste.
- Type of containment, i.e. loose or bagged.
- Time and place of transfer.
- Name and address of transferor and transferee.
- Whether the transferor is the producer or importer of the waste.
- If relevant, which authorised transport purpose applies.

Under normal circumstances all waste will be collected by arrangement either by the council or a local, registered carrier. The waste will generally be of the same composition for the duration of the contract.

As mentioned earlier, the definition of waste produced by kennels is under review, therefore it is worth checking with the local authority to clarify local policy.

5.6   GAS SAFETY REGULATIONS

The Gas Safety (Installation & Use) Regulations 1994 were introduced to try and prevent and reduce the amount of dangerous gas appliances in use; these include fires, cookers, boilers, laundry equipment, etc.

The regulations are complex but the basic guidelines are simple. These are:

- To ensure that any gas appliance or installation pipework at a place of work is maintained in a safe condition.

- It is the duty of any person who owns a gas appliance or any installation in a premise or part of a premise let by him to ensure that the appliance and installation is in a safe condition.

- A registered and qualified person should check the appliance and installation at intervals of not more than 12 months. A record should be kept of the inspection and any recommendations or works carried out.

   The records should be kept and made available by a tenant or staff member who may be affected by the use and operation of the appliance.

5.7 ELECTRICITY AT WORK REGULATIONS

The Electricity at Work Regulations 1989 were introduced in April 1990 and designed to take into account changes in technological developments and more importantly brought a legal compliance to all.

The main changes were:

- The Regulations apply to all places of work.
- Unlike earlier Regulations, there are no in-built exemptions.

Inspections

It is a legal requirement that the premises provide a safe environment for staff, public and any other visitors and that an inspection of the entire wiring system is carried out every 3 to 5 years.

Obviously, a new installation that has not been modified or tampered with is far safer than an installation that is 30 years old and has had several modifications over this period.

Portable Appliance Testing

The testing and recording of electrical portable appliances is a procedure that is normally carried out every 12 months for most light commercial operations; it is a legal requirement.

Each appliance and if applicable its power lead is tested by a suitably trained person or electrician; on completion of the test it will either pass, or fail and need corrective works. Once these have been carried out it will be tested again and either pass or fail.

Once a 'pass' standard has been reached, this will vary for each appliance. A label will be stuck/attached to the appliance with its own unique number or code for identification purposes and should be logged either in a book or on a disk, and should be kept in a safe place.

5.8 FIRE PRECAUTIONS (WORKPLACE) REGULATIONS 1997

On 1 December 1997 the Fire Precautions (Workplace) Regulations took effect with explicit requirements for every organisation with five or more employees to carry out a written fire risk assessment.

The assessment is to ensure that all areas of potential risk have been identified.

In the main this will cover:

- Identification the areas where fires are likely to occur.

- Provision of measures to minimise the possibility of a fire starting.

- Ensuring that fire protection systems, escape routes, etc. allow escape to a safe place.

Every area should be assessed separately and a judgement should be made with regard to the type of combustible materials and possible sources of ignition, types of doors, i.e. should standard doors be replaced with fire rated ones, availability of fire extinguishers, etc.

5.9 CONTROL OF SUBSTANCES HAZARDOUS TO HEALTH REGULATIONS 1994

The Control of Substances Hazardous to Health Regulations 1994 (COSHH) apply to potentially harmful substances. The COSSH provisions cover practically all substances that are harmful to health at work e.g. disinfectants, kennel waste etc.

The act is broken down into six main provisions:

1. Assessment - No employee should be exposed to substances hazardous to health unless an assessment has been carried out. The data sheets provided by the chemical manufacturers will provide the general information required.

2. Prevention or control - Once substances to health have been identified the employer is must prevent or control it by various means such as, substitution, elimination or ventilation etc.

3. Maintenance and testing of equipment - Employers must ensure that employees use any control measures in force. The employer is responsible for ensuring that all equipment is inspected, tested and a record is kept of this.

4. Monitoring - Employers must monitor employees who have been exposed to hazardous substances.

5. Health surveillance - If employees are exposed to substances which may have been a contributory factor to ill health e.g. dermatitis and disinfectants it may be appropriate to arrange a health surveillance programme. This can range from a full medical check - up to self inspection.

6. Information, training and instruction. - Employees who are exposed to hazardous substances must be given the adequate training, information and instruction to know the risks involved to their health and how to use control measures.

THANK YOU FOR READING "ESSENTIAL KENNEL DESIGN".

We hope you found this book informative & that it has helped you through some of the difficult decisions that a kennel owner has to make.

Do you have any <u>comments</u> on the contents of this book **?**
How has this advice <u>helped</u> you **?**
Are there areas you would like <u>incorporated</u> in future editions **?**

Would you like details or advice on <u>Cattery</u> design & specification **?**

<u>If you would like advice or consultancy, do please contact us:</u>

Essential Kennel Design
P.O Box 146
Chipping Norton D.O
Oxfordshire
OX7 6WA

☎   01993 831405

LIST OF SUPPLIERS, EQUIPMENT & REFERENCE PUBLICATIONS.

ARCHITECTS

Mr Barry Coupe
Forum Architects & Project Management
Palace Coach House
Palace Street
Newmarket
Suffolk, CB8 8EP
Tel: 01638 665757

LAUNDRY EQUIPMENT

John Laithwaite Associates Ltd
Meadowcroft Lane
Halifax Road
Ripponden
West Yorkshire, HX6 4AJ
Tel: 01422 822282. E-mail: info@jlajla.com

FLOOR FINISHES
Epoxy   **Resins -**

Seamless Surfaces	Flowcrete Systems Ltd.
Coppice side	The Flooring Technology Centre
Brownhills	Booth Lane
West Midlands	Moston
WS8 7EY	Sandbach
Tel: 01543 370057	Cheshire,
	CW11 9QF
	Tel: 01270 753000

Tiles -

Architectural Ceramics (UK) Ltd	Pilkington's Tiles Ltd
Unit 3	P.O. Box 4
Monarch Industrial Park	Clifton Junction
198 Kings Road	Manchester
Tyseley	M27 8LP
Birmingham, B11 2AP	Tel: 0161 727 1111
Tel: 0121 706 6456	

KENNEL METALWORK

Croft Engineering
2 Swan Meadow Mill
Swan Meadow Road
Wigan
Lancs.
WN3 5BD
Tel: 01942 497677
www.croft-kennels.co.uk

Coningsby Metals Ltd
Silver Street
Coningsby
Lincolnshire
LN4 4SQ
Tel: 01526 42141

ACOUSTIC CEILING TILES

Torvale Building Products
Pembridge
Leominster
Herefordshire
HR6 91A
Tel: 01544 388262

Armstrong World Industries Ltd
38 Market Square
Uxbridge
Middlesex
UB8 1NG
Tel: 0800 371849

CATERING & KITCHEN EQUIPMENT

W & G Sissons
Carrwood Road
Sheepbridge Trading Estate
Chesterfield
S41 9QB
Tel: 01246 450255

Corsair Manufacturing Ltd
Beaumont Close
Beaumont Industrial Estate
Banbury
Oxfordshire, OX16 7SH
Tel: 01295 267021

DRAINAGE CHANNELS

Aco Technologies plc
Hitchin Road
Shefford
Bedfordshire, SG17 5TE
Tel: 01462 816666

Clarksteel
Station Road
Yaxley
Peterborough, PE7 3EG
Tel: 01733 240811

ACRYLATED RUBBER WALL PAINTS

ICI Paints
Wexham Road
Slough
SL2 5DS
Tel: 01753 534225

Johnstons Heavy Duty Coatings
Kalon Paints
Huddersfield Road
Birstall
Batley
West Yorkshire
WF17 9XA
Tel: 01924 420202

WASTE WATER TREATMENT SYSTEMS

Burnham Environmental Services
27 Brightstowe Road
Burnham–on-Sea
Somerset
TA8 2HW
Tel: 01278 786104

Balmoral Mouldings
Balmoral Park
Loirston
Aberdeen
Tel: 01224 859100

COMPOSIT BOARD MANUFACTURERS

Trespa UK Ltd
Grosvenor House
Hollinswood Road
Central Park
Telford
TF2 9TW

Perstorp Wareite Ltd
Aycliffe Industrial Park
NewtonAycliffe
County Durham
DL5 6EF
Tel: 01325 315141

USEFUL ADDRESSES

Asbestos Removal Contractors' Association
6 Parkway
Chelmsford
Essex
CM2 ONF
Tel: 01245 259774

British Association of Landscape Industries
Landscape House
9 Henry St
Keighley
WestYorkshire
BD21 3DR
Tel: 01535 606139

Croner CCH Group Ltd.
Croner House
145 London Road
Kingston upon Thames
Surrey KT2 6SR.
Tel: 0181 547 3333
Fax: 0181 547 2637
e-mail info@croner.co.uk
➢ (Croner's offer a wide range of specialist loose-leaf binders on a variety of subjects i.e. Waste Management, Premises Management, Health & Safety, etc.

Ordnance Survey
Romsey Road
Maybush
Southampton
Hampshire
S09 4DH
Tel: 023 8079 2000